From Nothing to Cosmos: God and Science

A Comprehensive Look at the Evidence for God

Robert J. Spitzer, S.J., Ph.D.

From Nothing to Cosmos: God and Science

A Comprehensive Look at the Evidence for God

A Study Guide for the DVD Presentation by Fr. Robert J. Spitzer, S.J., Ph.D.

Acknowledgements

I would like to thank Ms. Joan Jacoby for formatting this document with great precision. I am also most grateful to the Board and benefactors of the Magis Institute who made possible the lectures and this book.

Cover Art by Jim Breen

© 2013 Robert J. Spitzer/Magis Institute

This edition published by:

Magis Publications
2532 Dupont Drive
Irvine, CA 92612

www.magiscenter.com

Library of Congress Control Number: 2013948176

ISBN: 978-0-9838945-5-1

Printed in the United States of America

TABLE OF CONTENTS

INTRODUCTION

This book was written primarily as a comprehensive Study Guide to the DVD presentation *From Nothing to Cosmos: God and Science* by Fr. Robert J. Spitzer, S.J., Ph.D. (four one-hour episodes). It may also serve as a Study Guide for Fr. Spitzer's live presentation *Science, God, and Creation* (one two–hour episode). The following table shows the coverage of both series.

From Nothing to Cosmos	#1	#2	#3	#4	#5	#6	#7	#8	#9	
Science, God, Creation	#1	#2	#3	#4	#5		#7			Appendix

Those using this Study Guide for *Science, God, and Creation* may want to look over the seven topic areas covered in Chapters 6, 8, and 9 (response to Dawkins' objections, a metaphysical proof of God, explanation of the five transcendental desires and how they indicate a transphysical soul, why some scientists are atheists, the bible and science, evolution, and aliens). If you have an interest in these areas you may want to consider viewing *From Nothing to Cosmos*.

This Study Guide may also be used by itself. The answers to the study questions do not presuppose any knowledge from the DVD presentation – all the major concepts are explained in this book. Nevertheless, most people who are not familiar with the basic concepts of physics, cosmology, and metaphysics will derive benefit from the DVD presentation because it is more accessible and gives "the whole picture" in an engaging presentation.

This Study Guide not only reviews the major concepts from the DVD presentation, but also goes beyond them. It gives more detailed explanations of the data and concepts of physics, and provides step by step explanations of why it points to an intelligent Creator or to a transphysical dimension of human consciousness (a "soul"). It also fills out the proof for the existence of God mentioned in Episode Three of *From Nothing to Cosmos* (as a response to Richard Dawkins) and gives a more complete explanation of the five transcendental desires mentioned in Episode Four of *From Nothing to Cosmos*. Thus, the Study

Guide can be used for self-study or by teachers, catechists, and bible study leaders to give more detailed explanations of the content in the DVD presentations.

It may be helpful for teachers and catechists to make photocopies of the Power Points (at the beginning of each Chapter in this Study Guide) to distribute to participants before viewing the presentation. Though the Power Points are included in the DVD presentation, the photocopies can be a reminder of the materials as the presentation proceeds. Another option, of course, is for each student to have their own book so they can review all of the materials and have them for future reference.

The quotations from major scientists (presented after the questions and answers in Chapters One through Five and Seven) can be very enlightening and inspiring to students and discussion group participants, and having someone read them aloud can be particularly effective. All the references to the quotations along with brief biographies of the physicists and physicians are given after the quotations.

This material is suitable for seniors in high school, college students, and adult learners. If you are interested in teaching these materials to ninth or tenth grade students (either in a classroom, a confirmation retreat, or a catechism class), we recommend using the age appropriate DVD set and Faculty Resource Manual called *The Reason Series: What Science Says About God.*

If you, the reader, have a general understanding of these concepts, and would be comfortable presenting them, we would greatly appreciate your making this offer to your Director of Religious Education or to the Director of your college campus ministry office. These materials have been effectively used in home bible study groups for both parishes and college ministry – as a supplement to bible study. Many participants find this evidence to be supportive and expansive of their biblical faith.

We would appreciate your comments on this book and presentation. Feel free to comment by visiting our website www.magisreasonfaith.org and clicking "contact us." Please peruse the additional available materials while you are there.

What Can Science Do and What Can't It Do?

(In both *Science, God and Creation* and *From Nothing to Cosmos* – Episode #1)

Outline of Chapter One Content and Power Points

Power Point #1.1

THE HORIZONS AND LIMITS OF SCIENCE

1. Science *cannot* disprove God.
2. Scientific theories are open to modification.

   And therefore, science cannot be sure it knows everything about the universe.

3. Science *can* give evidence of the beginning of the universe, implying a creation.

Power Point #1.2
Four Steps from Beginning to Creation

1. Beginning of physical time = the absolute beginning of physical reality.
2. Before the absolute beginning of physical reality - - physical reality = nothing.
3. Nothing = nothing; nothing can only do nothing.
4. When physical reality = nothing, then physical reality cannot move itself from nothing to something.

Therefore, something else (something transcending physical reality) had to move it from nothing to something - - a Creator.

Review Questions and Answers (Chapter One)

1. **What kind of method is used in science?**

    Answer: Inductive method (moving from particulars to universals). Notice that this is different from deductive method which moves from general principles to particular conclusions. It is important to know the limits of inductive method, because it means that science cannot know if it knows everything about the physical universe. Why? Because science can never know whether it has discovered every particular datum necessary to have a complete explanation of the universe. It must always be open to new discoveries (and even to surprising new discoveries). Science cannot know what it has not yet discovered since it has not yet discovered it.

2. **What are the limits to scientific data?**

    Answer: Scientific data must come from observation. This means that it is limited to physical reality and the physical universe (which are observable). Anything which is beyond our observational capability is beyond scientific method. Thus, for example, transcendent realities or spiritual realities which may be beyond our observational capacity, are not within the scope of natural science.

3. **Why can't physics render a negative conclusion about God?**

    Answer: For two reasons. First, if science is limited to data from within our universe (what can be directly observed), and God is beyond our universe, then science cannot disprove what is beyond its source of data. Since God is always beyond a scientific source of data, science cannot make a judgment about whether there is a reality beyond its data source.

    Secondly, it is much more difficult to disprove something by observational method than to prove it. Why? If you want to prove that something exists by observational method (say, an alien), one need only observe one of them. However, if one wants to disprove aliens by observational method, one will have to observe everything that there is to observe, know that one has done this completely and correctly, be certain that all realities are within our powers of observation, and then notice that aliens are not there. Needless to say, this is virtually impossible to accomplish.

4. **If science cannot negate the reality of God, how can it actually give evidence for God?**

    Answer: Science can show an absolute limit to past time

in our universe by means of space-time geometry proofs and the second law of thermodynamics – entropy (see the questions below in this section). These two kinds of data are *observational* data from within the *physical universe*, and therefore are within the domain of scientific method. This absolute limit to past time (termed an absolute beginning) is the beginning of physical time itself, and since physical time must condition all physical reality, it is a beginning of physical reality itself. Prior to this absolute beginning, physical reality was literally nothing. Since nothing cannot do anything, we must conclude that when physical reality was nothing, it could not have moved itself into existence – and therefore, something else would have had to have done this – something transcending our universe. This "transcendent something" is called a "Creator."

5. Can science explain everything about everything?

Answer: No. Science cannot explain everything about everything because scientific data is limited to what can be observed in our universe, therefore science cannot know if there is (or is not) a reality (or realities) beyond the universe and our observational powers.

6. Can scientists ever know that they have explained everything about everything in our universe?

Answer: No. Because science is an inductive discipline, (which means that it moves from particulars to universals) and scientists cannot ever know whether they have discovered all the particulars that are ingredient to a complete explanation of the universe. They cannot know what they have not discovered until they have discovered it. (See above question #1.)

7. What should you think about scientists who claim they know everything about everything in the universe (and even outside of it)?

Answer: You should put no credence in that viewpoint, because these two claims lie outside of the methodological limits of science.

8. **Is it true to say that science can never disprove God, but that it can give evidence for God (a transcendent Creator)?**

   Answer: Yes, that is true. (See the four questions immediately above).

9. **What does an absolute beginning in physics signify?**

   Answer: An absolute beginning signifies a beginning of physical time. Since physical time conditions all physical reality (that is, physical reality does not exist without physical time), the absolute beginning of physical time must also be the absolute beginning of physical reality. Prior to the absolute beginning of physical reality, physical reality would have to have been nothing. It would not have existed in any respect.

10. **Prior to an absolute beginning, what was physical reality?**

    Answer: Absolutely NOTHING. (see above).

11. **What is nothing?**

    Answer: Several physicists have recently tried to redefine "nothing" – as a zero energy condition of the quantum field, the law of gravitation, or something else. But, as noted above, an absolute beginning of physical reality means the beginning of physical time itself. This means that no physical reality could have existed. Clearly a zero energy quantum field is a physical reality (and not nothing), and it would not have existed prior to an absolute beginning of physical reality. If the law of gravitation is thought to exist independently of physical reality, then it would have to be some kind of mental reality – like a divine idea or a platonic idea, but this begs the question of a mind that can create such an idea – which sounds surprisingly similar to a Creator.

12. **What can nothing do?**

    Answer. Nothing.

13. **Why is this answer significant for the question about a Creator of the universe?**

    Answer: If we do not make "nothing" into something (or sneak something into nothing), then we know that this nothing could not have done anything. Now if it could not have done anything, then it could not have moved itself from nothing to something. How then did the universe move from nothing to something at the absolute beginning, if physical reality could not have done it? It must be that something beyond (transcending) physical reality did it, and this "transcendent something" is called a Creator.

14. **If the universe could not have moved itself from nothing to something when it was nothing, then how could it have come to be real?**

    Answer. Something ELSE would have had to have done it, and that something else would have to transcend the universe (and physical reality as a whole). (See question #13 above).

15. **Is it correct to say that if physics can prove an absolute beginning of the universe (or a multiverse that spawned it), it also implies the existence of a transcendent Creator?**

    Answer: Yes, because a beginning implies a point at which the universe (and even its physical time) came into existence; and prior to that point, it was literally nothing. Now, since nothing is nothing, and nothing can only do nothing, then the universe could not have moved itself from nothing to something when it was nothing; therefore, something outside the universe (transcending the universe) would have had to have moved the universe from nothing to something.

The Big Bang Theory and the Modern Universe

(In both *Science, God and Creation* and *From Nothing to Cosmos* – Episode #1)

Outline of Chapter Two Content and Power Points

Power Point #2.1

The BIG BANG Theory

13.8 Billion Years Ago the Universe Begins Expansion

Fr. Georges Lemaître

Hubble's Redshifts

COBE and WMAP Satellites

Power Point #2.2

Description of the Modern Universe

Mass-energy of universe:

- **4.6% visible matter (emits and absorbs electromagnetic radiation/light)**
- **23% dark matter (no e-m radiation, but gravitational effects)**
- **72.4% dark energy (field-like with strong repulsive force)**

Four Forces:

- **electromagnetic force, gravitational force,**
- **strong nuclear force, and weak force**

Constituents of visible matter:

- 10^{53} kg of visible matter = 10^{80} baryons
- 10^{22} stars in 10^{11} galaxies

Review Questions and Answers (Chapter Two)

16. Among Einstein's many contributions to physics, what was his most important cosmological discovery?

Answer: The General Theory of Relativity, which integrated mass, energy, space, and time. It was the first comprehensive, organic cosmological explanation of the universe as a whole. Though Newton did have a theory of the universe as a whole, he separated space, time, mass, and energy, and hence his explanation was not organic and only partial.

17. What was the datum that could not be explained by Einstein's steady state assumption within the General Theory of Relativity?

Answer: The radial velocity of extra-galactic nebulae (the extraordinary recessional velocities of light sources outside of our galaxy). Today, we know that these nebulae (light sources) are other galaxies and galactic systems. They were moving away from our galaxy much too quickly to be explained by the steady-state assumption within the general theory of relativity.

18. What does the "steady-state assumption of the General Theory of Relativity" refer to?

Answer: That the universe as a whole is neither expanding nor contracting, that is, the universe as a whole remains at the same volume throughout the course of its existence.

19. What was the profession of Georges Lemaître?

Answer: He was both a Catholic Priest and a Theoretical Physicist with a specialization in Cosmology.

20. Why did Lemaître propose his expanding universe hypothesis to Einstein?

Answer: Assuming that the universe expanded much like a balloon being blown up, the high velocities of extra-galactic nebulae could be explained with almost perfect mathematical accuracy. Lemaitre noticed that if space was stretching (growing), like the elastic of a balloon being blown up, then the further a galaxy is from us (the observer), the greater its recessional velocity must be. Why? Take out a rubber band and put it next to a ruler. Now draw a dot on the rubber band at point zero; another dot at one inch; and yet another dot at two inches. Now, take the rubber band and hold it with your left hand at point zero. With your right hand stretch the rubber band so that the dot that was at two inches is now at four inches. Evidently the dot which was at two inches from origin has expanded another two inches (to the four inch mark). But notice that the dot which was at the one inch mark has only moved to the two inch mark (an expansion of only one inch). Thus, if space as a whole is growing like a balloon (or like our rubber band), the further away a galaxy is from our galaxy (at point zero on the ruler), the more it expands per unit time. Since expansion per unit time is recessional velocity, Lemaitre is right – the further away the galaxy is, the greater its recessional velocity. This insight will be very important when we explain the Borde-Vilenkin-Guth proof below.

21. How old is the Universe?

Answer: 13.8 Billion years +/- 200 million years.

22. How did Hubble advance Lemaître's theory of a universal expansion?

Answer: He discovered precise observational evidence for it -- namely, the red shifting of galaxies (and specifically, an increase in red shifting in more distant galaxies). This indicated that the further a galaxy was from us, the greater its recessional velocity. He also made a very comprehensive survey of the observational sky. The precision of his observations led to a replacement of the Lemaitre Constant with the Hubble Constant.

23. What is a red shift?

Answer: When light is emitted from a luminous object moving away from me (the observer), the frequency of that light will be shifted toward the red end of the spectrum (the infrared end of the spectrum which has very low frequency – low intensity), because as the object moves away from me, that movement "de-intensifies" the frequency of the light (the speed of light never changes, but the frequency of light is effected by an object moving away from me or towards me). Conversely, if light is emitted by an object moving towards me (the observer), then the spectrum of that light will be shifted toward the blue end of the spectrum (the ultraviolet end of the spectrum which has higher frequency – more intensity), because the objects motion towards me intensifies the frequency of the light. This is called a "blue shift." The greater the red shift, the faster an object is moving away from me, and the greater the blue shift, the faster an object is moving towards me.

24. Hubble discovered that the further the luminous object was away from him, the greater was the red shift. What does this mean?

Answer: The greater the red shift, the faster an object is moving away from me (the observer), so what Hubble discovered was that the further a galaxy is from us (the observer), the faster it is moving away from us. This can be explained by Lemaitre's theory that space as a whole is stretching (growing) like the elastic of a balloon. Recall the rubber band experiment above – the farther away the dot from the point of origin, the faster it moves away from the point of origin.

25. What other confirmatory evidence for the "Big Bang" theory has been discovered since the time of Edwin Hubble?

Answer: The discovery by Arno Penzias and Robert Wilson of a 2.7-degree Kelvin uniformly distributed radiation (throughout our entire universe) which could have only originated from an early fundamental cosmological event. Furthermore, there is considerable corroborating evidence from two satellites -- The Cosmic Background Explorer Satellite (the COBE satellite) as well as the Wilkinson Microwave Anisotropy Probe (WMAP satellite).

26. Why do physicists believe that the 2.7-degree Kelvin uniform radiation had to have occurred in a cosmic event near the beginning of the universe?

Answer: Since the radiation is uniformly distributed (virtually the same throughout the entire universe) it could not have originated at a particular place in an already-expanded universe. If it had, the shock wave would have moved away from the epicenter of the explosion and it would have rushed from one place to another place growing weaker as it did so. Thus, it would not have been uniformly distributed everywhere in the universe. So the uniform radiation must have originated at a point when it could be everywhere distributed (and would cool at the same rate everywhere in the universe). The only time at which this could have occurred is very near to the beginning of the universe itself.

27. What are the four forces in our universe?

Answer: The electromagnetic force which explains electrical activity. The strong nuclear force which binds protons together in the nucleus of an atom. The weak force which is responsible for radiation and particle decay. The gravitational force which is explained by the curvature of the space-time field in the General Theory of Relativity. It is responsible for attraction of massive bodies at a distance.

28. What does the electromagnetic force do?

Answer: It is the source of all electrical activity. It has the power to attract and repel charges which creates force that can move things, change things, give rise to light and heat, as well as make things strong and hard, and give things shape.

29. What does the strong nuclear force do?

Answer: The strong nuclear force binds together protons in the nucleus of an atom. We know of the existence of this force because protons (being of similar charge) should repel each other, since this is the ordinary dynamic of the electromagnetic force. Then how can protons, as it were, "stick together" (when they should be repelling)? There must be a stronger force of attraction than the electromagnetic force of repulsion. This force only becomes strong when protons are in exceedingly close proximity to one another under high pressures and temperatures (i.e. nuclear fusion).

30. What does the weak force do?

Answer: It causes radioactive decay, particle decay, which results in radiation and is, as will later be seen, responsible for the way in which the universe emerged.

31. What does the gravitational force do?

Answer: Gravitational force is the force of attraction among massive bodies in the universe. It increases in proportion to the masses which are in proximity to one another, and it also increases with shorter distances among those bodies. Thus, the more massive the bodies and the shorter the distance among them, the stronger the gravitational force. Since the time of Einstein, we no longer consider gravity to be a force (as Newton did) -- today we know that the effects of gravitation are produced by the curved geometry of the space-time continuum. The greater the curvature, the stronger the gravitational effect. Greater density of mass-energy causes greater curvature of the space-time continuum.

32. Are these four forces the only constituents of our universe?

Answer: No. The four forces inhere in what is called "visible matter" (mass-energy that emits luminescent, electromagnetic, nuclear, and other energy -- that is, matter that can do something). This is only 4.6% of the total mass-energy in our universe. There are two other major sources of mass-energy -- dark matter (23%) and dark energy (72.4%). [1]

33. Is space simply an empty vacuum?

Answer: No. Space in the General Theory of Relativity is a highly dynamic field. It is capable of adjusting its coordinate system and curvature in proportion to the density of Mass-Energy within it (mass and energy are essentially convertible to one another, and so we might refer to it in combination as Mass-Energy). Thus, the density of Mass-Energy can actually "collapse" the coordinate structure of

---

[1] The recent Planck spacecraft data (March-April 2013) made slight revisions to the data used in this presentation recorded earlier. According to the new data, the universe is 13.8 billion years old (instead of 13.7 billion years old as previously thought) and the proportion of visible matter, dark matter, and dark energy has also been revised. According to the Planck spacecraft the current estimate of visible matter is now 4.9% (instead of 4.6%), dark matter is 26.8% (instead of 23%), and dark energy is 68.3% (instead of 72.4%). This was not corrected throughout this book because the video presentation uses the older figures.

the spatial continuum and "pull together" the coordinate structure surrounding the collapsed area (much like when you pinch a table cloth and pull it up, you notice that you not only alter the area being pinched, but also the surrounding area of the table cloth -- notice, too, that the closer that an area is to the one being pinched, the more altered it is).

34. Describe the dynamics of Einstein's space-time continuum.

Answer: As noted in the previous question, the density of Mass-Energy can affect the coordinate structure of the spatial continuum. The greater the density, the more the collapse of the coordinate structure (not only where the Mass-Energy is located, but also in the surrounding area -- like the table cloth). Strange as it may seem, when the coordinate structure of space collapses, it does not only affect the spatial continuum -- it also collapses the coordinate structure of the Mass-Energy within it (that is why, for example, an entire star can be collapsed into 10^{-33} centimeters at the base of a black hole. The star takes on the significantly collapsed coordinate structure of the spatial continuum where the density of Mass-Energy is high). This means that you cannot look at Mass-Energy and Space-Time as being two different "things" in the sense of Newton's Universe. There must be an underlying organic unity between Mass-Energy and Space-Time which enables the density of the former to collapse the coordinate structure of the latter while enabling the coordinate structure of the latter to determine the coordinate structure of the former. Unity among the constituent parts of our universe seems to be more fundamental than the constituent parts themselves.

35. What is dark energy?

Answer: Dark energy is not like dark matter. In fact, it is not like matter in any respect. It is like a field which "attaches itself" to our dynamic space-time continuum and causes it to stretch or expand very rapidly. This stretching or expanding has an accelerative effect. Some people doubt the existence of Dark Energy, and think that it is just a fudge factor that scientists have invented to explain faster than expected inflation. A majority of physicists believe that Dark Energy exists. Over a decade ago, astronomers observing the brightness of distant supernovae realized that the expansion of the universe appeared to be accelerating. They attributed the acceleration to the repulsive force associated with dark energy. In September 2012 a team of astronomers at the University of Portsmouth and LMU University Munich, determined that the likelihood of the existence of dark energy stands at 99.996 per cent. The team released their findings after two years of study and re-verification of the *Integrated Sachs-Wolfe effect*; the theory that first gave credence to Dark Energy. Dr. Alan Guth theorized that Dark Energy was a very probable source of a cool inflationary period immediately after the Big Bang, which is necessary to explain the distribution of mass and galaxies (as well as several other phenomena) throughout the universe.

36. What is dark matter?

Answer: Dark matter resembles visible matter in one important respect -- it interacts with the space-time field in the same way -- that is, it causes gravitational effects ("attraction" effects). As noted above, dark energy is causing the space between galaxies to stretch (grow) at an accelerated rate; so the question arises: Why don't the galaxies expand or grow at the same accelerated rate (which would make them fly apart)?" Because the attraction produced by both dark matter and visible matter within the galaxies (where the density of mass-energy is much higher than in intergalactic space) counteracts the effects of dark energy and keeps the galaxies together.

Quotations and References from Major Scientists

I. **Quotations**

    A. **Fr. Georges Lemaitre's Description of the Initial Moment of the Universe:**

        We can compare space-time to an open, conic cup. The bottom of the cup is the origin of atomic disintegration; it is the first instant at the bottom of space-time, the now which has no yesterday because, yesterday, there was no space.[2]

    B. **Personal Communication of Einstein to Fr. Georges Lemaitre Concerning the Expansion of the Universe as a Whole:**

        This is the most beautiful and satisfactory explanation of creation to which I have ever listened.[3]

    C. **NASA Biography of Edwin Hubble Explaining the Significance of his Survey of the Heaven's for Confirming the Big Bang Theory as well as Lemaitre's/ Hubble's Law (the greater the distance galaxies are from one another, the faster they are moving away from one another):**

        The most astonishing discovery Hubble made resulted from his study of the spectra of 46 galaxies, and in particular of the Doppler velocities of those galaxies relative to our own Milky Way galaxy. What Hubble found was that the farther apart galaxies are from each other, the faster they move away from each other. Based on this observation, Hubble concluded that the universe expands uniformly. Several scientists had also posed this theory based on Einstein's General Relativity, but Hubble's data, published in 1929, helped convince the scientific community.[4]

---

[2] Lemaitre. 1943 p 133
[3] Topper. 2013 p 175
[4] NASA Biography of Edwin Powell Hubble. http://asd.gsfc.nasa.gov/archive/hubble/overview/hubble_bio.html

D. NASA Summary of Discovery and Significance of Cosmic Microwave Background Radiation:

The existence of the CMB radiation was first predicted by Ralph Alpher, Robert Herman, and George Gamow in 1948, as part of their work on Big Bang Nucleosynthesis. It was first observed inadvertently in 1965 by Arno Penzias and Robert Wilson at the Bell Telephone Laboratories in Murray Hill, New Jersey. The radiation was acting as a source of excess noise in a radio receiver they were building. Coincidentally, researchers at nearby Princeton University, led by Robert Dicke and including Dave Wilkinson of the WMAP science team, were devising an experiment to find the CMB. When they heard about the Bell Labs result they immediately realized that the CMB had been found. The result was a pair of papers in the Astrophysical Journal (vol. 142 of 1965): one by Penzias and Wilson detailing the observations, and one by Dicke, Peebles, Roll, and Wilkinson giving the cosmological interpretation. Penzias and Wilson shared the 1978 Nobel prize in physics for their discovery.[5]

E. NASA Report on the Data from the COBE (Cosmic Background Explorer) Satellite Confirming the Contemporary Big Bang Theory from the Cosmic Microwave Background Radiation:

FIRAS (Far Infrared Absolute Spectrophotometer) The cosmic microwave background (CMB) spectrum is that of a nearly perfect blackbody with a temperature of 2.725 +/- 0.002 K. This observation matches the predictions of the hot Big Bang theory extraordinarily well, and indicates that nearly all of the radiant energy of the Universe was released within the first year after the Big Bang.[6]

---

[5] http://map.gsfc.nasa.gov/universe/bb_tests_cmb.html
[6] NASA Report on Findings of the COBE Satellite. http://lambda.gsfc.nasa.gov/product/cobe/

F. Report on NASA Press Conference by Director Charles Bennett (February 11, 2003) Concerning the Data of the WMAP Satellite Confirming the Contemporary Big Bang Theory:

Astronomers announced findings from the space-based Microwave Anisotropy Probe (MAP) observatory. Principal investigator of MAP, Charles Bennett, noted that the data revealed that the universe had cooled enough for matter to condense and form the first stars just 200 million years after the big bang. This enabled astronomers to calculate the age of the observable universe at 13.7+ billion years old, plus or minus 200 million years. These findings provide the strongest support to date for the Big Bang theory of the creation of the observable universe, along with a verification of the inflationary era in the first few seconds of the universe's existence.[7]

II. References

Barr, Stephen. 2003 *Modern Physics and Ancient Faith* (Notre Dame: Notre Dame University Press).

Hubble, Edwin. 1929. "A Relation between Distance and Radial Velocity among Extra-galactic Nebulae." *Proceedings of the National Academy of Sciences* 15, pp. 168-73.

Lemaitre, Georges. 1943 *The Primeval Atom* (New York: The University Press).

Penzias, Arno A. and Wilson, Robert W. 1965. "A Measurement of Excess Antenna Temperature at 4080 Mc/s." *Astrophysical Journal* 142, pp. 419-21.

Spitzer, Robert. 2010 *New Proofs for the Existence of God: Contributions of Contemporary Physics and Philosophy* (Grand Rapids: Eerdmans).

Topper, David. 2013 *How Einstein Created Relativity Out of Physics and Astronomy* (New York: Springer).

---

[7] Report on NASA Press Conference www.space.com/scienceastronomy/map_ discovery_030211

Brief Biographies of Key Scientists

Albert Einstein: Albert Einstein was a German-born theoretical physicist who developed the general theory of relativity, one of the two pillars of modern physics (alongside quantum mechanics).While best known for his mass-energy equivalence formula $E = mc^2$ (which has been dubbed "the world's most famous equation"), he received the 1921 Nobel Prize in Physics "for his services to theoretical physics, and especially for his discovery of the law of the photoelectric effect. The latter was pivotal in establishing quantum theory.[8]

Fr. Georges Lemaitre: Georges Henri Joseph Édouard Lemaître was a Belgian priest, astronomer, and professor of physics at the Catholic University of Louvain. He was the first person to propose the theory of the expansion of the Universe, widely misattributed to Edwin Hubble. He was also the first to derive what is now known as Hubble's law and made the first estimation of what is now called the Hubble constant, which he published in 1927, two years before Hubble's article. Lemaître also proposed what became known as the Big Bang theory of the origin of the Universe, which he called his 'hypothesis of the primeval atom.[9]

Edwin Powell Hubble: Edwin Hubble was an American astronomer who played a crucial role in establishing the field of extragalactic astronomy and is generally regarded as one of the most important observational cosmologists of the 20th century. Hubble is known for showing that the recessional velocity of a galaxy increases with its distance from the earth, implying the universe is expanding. Known as "Hubble's law," this relation had been discovered previously by Georges Lemaitre, a Belgian priest/astronomer who published his work in a less visible journal. There is still much controversy surrounding the issue and some argue that it should be referred to as "Lemaitre's law" although this change has not taken hold in the astronomy community.[10]

Dr. Arno Penzias (b. 1933 in Germany) fled, at age six, with his family to the U.S. to escape the Nazis. He became a U.S. citizen in 1946, and earned his Ph.D. in physics in 1962 from Columbia University. In 1964, with Robert Wilson, Penzias encountered unexplained radio noise coming equally from every part of the sky while using the Bell Labs radio telescope in Holmden, New Jersey. They realized it was Cosmic Microwave Background Radiation remaining from the Big Bang, confirming that it had occurred. Both Penzias and Wilson received the 1978 Nobel Prize in Physics.

---

[8] Wikipedia 2013 "Albert Einstein" http://en.wikipedia.org/wiki/Albert_Lemaitre
[9] Wikipedia 2013 "Georges Lemaitre" http://en.wikipedia.org/wiki/Georges_Lemaitre
[10] Wikipedia 2012 "Edwin Hubble" http://en.wikipedia.org/wiki/Edwin_Hubble

CHAPTER THREE

The Borde-Vilenkin-Guth Proof
for a Beginning of the Universe
(and all Multiverses)

(In both *Science, God and Creation* and *From Nothing to Cosmos* – Episode #2)

Outline of Chapter Three Content and Power Points

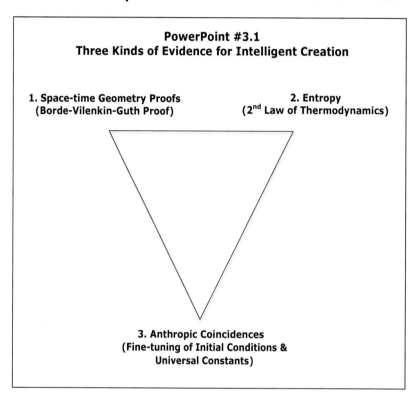

PowerPoint #3.1
Three Kinds of Evidence for Intelligent Creation

1. Space-time Geometry Proofs
(Borde-Vilenkin-Guth Proof)

2. Entropy
(2nd Law of Thermodynamics)

3. Anthropic Coincidences
(Fine-tuning of Initial Conditions &
Universal Constants)

Power Point #3.2

SPACE-TIME GEOMETRY PROOFS

1. The 1993 Borde-Vilenkin Proof
(five conditions).

2. The 1999 comprehensive modeling
of inflationary universes/multiverses (Alan
Guth).

3. The 2003 Borde-Vilenkin-Guth
Proof (the B-V-G Theorem) – only one
condition; physics of universe is not relevant.

Power Point #3.3

5 Steps of the B-V-G Proof

1. The greater the distance a galaxy is from us, the faster will be
   its recessional velocity (the ruler and the rubber band).
2. The further into the future we go, the greater will be the
   recessional velocity of galaxies.
3. The relative velocity of projectiles (like a rocket ship) must
   decrease as recessional velocities increase (into the future).
4. The further we go into the past, the faster the relative
   velocities must have been.
5. At some point in the past, all relative velocities will reach the
   speed of light (the maximum velocity of physical energy in the
   universe).

Power Point #3.4

Conclusions of the B-V-G Proof

1. There is only one condition of this proof - - the average rate of expansion of the universe is greater than zero.
2. The B-V-G Proof applies to our universe, all multiverses, and all bouncing universes (including those in the higher dimensional space of string theory).

   Therefore the B-V-G Proof strongly indicates an absolute beginning of all physical reality

---

Review Questions and Answers (Chapter Three)

37. What is a space-time geometry proof?

Answer. The highly dynamic structure of Space-Time (see 34 and 35 above) allows us to make predictions about what the Space-Time continuum must do under certain conditions. Thus, the typical form of a Space-Time Geometry Proof is "if condition x, condition y, and condition z are real in the universe, then there must be a beginning of that universe." First one must prove the major premise (the "if -- then" part of the proof) which normally entails both mathematics and logic (as we shall see below). Then, we must prove the minor premise (the part of the proof which shows that each of the conditions *do in fact exist* in our universe). This part of the proof must be done by observations or experiments based on observations. If both the major and minor premises can be shown to be correct, then the conclusion would naturally follow as correct.

38. What is quantum cosmology?

Answer: There can be no space smaller than 1.616×10^{-33} centimeters (the Planck length), because this is an intrinsic limit within the Space-Time continuum. Furthermore, there can be no time smaller than 5.3×10^{-44} seconds (the Planck time) which is also an intrinsic limit within the Space-Time continuum. This leaves us with an interesting paradox: How do we get back to zero seconds? It also leaves us with the question of whether it is possible in principle to ever have a Planck era (some point prior to the Planck length and Planck time). If such an era were to be possible, it could not happen through a Space-Time continuum described by the General Theory of Relativity (because the minimums of space and time in GTR would have to be violated). Furthermore, in GTR, gravitational effects are explained through the Space-Time continuum. Thus, if we are to get to a period that violates the two Planck limits, we will have to do it in "quantum" space-time, so to speak, and we will have to explain gravitational effects in some way other than the Space-Time continuum. This is done by unifying the Gravitational Force with the other three forces of the Grand Unified Field (Electromagnetic force, Strong Nuclear force, and Weak force). This has been theoretically and mathematically accomplished (but not observationally verified) in two hypothetical systems: One, String Theory (and its 11-dimensional integrated configuration -- M Theory) and Two, Loop Quantum Gravity (a theory of integration that does not require an 11-dimensional Space -- higher dimensional space -- which is quite theoretical).

39. Give a general description of string theory.

Answer: String theory is one hypothetical system of quantum cosmology that unifies the gravitational force with the other three forces in the Grand Unified Field (Electromagnetic force, Strong Nuclear force, and Weak force). It proposes an 11-dimensional configuration (10 spatial dimensions plus time) of one-dimensional vibrating strings. This hypothetical system can explain all forces, particles, and even spins of particles (which would occur when a Space-Time continuum comes into being and the three forces of the GUFT can interact through it -- and Gravitational effects can be explained by it). The mathematics of this theory is very complex, but it seems to be remarkably explanatory. It has still not been observationally verified.

40. What is the general structure of Borde and Vilenkin's 1993 Space-Time Geometry Proof?

Answer: They showed that if 5 conditions were met, any

inflationary universe would have to have a beginning. Thus, the form is:

If condition 1, 2, 3, 4 & 5 are all true for our universe, then our universe would have to have a beginning in past time.

Our universe does meet conditions 1, 2, 3, 4, & 5. Therefore, our universe does have a beginning in past time.

Borde and Vilenkin discovered a possible loophole in condition number 3 (called the "weak energy condition") in 1997. It is highly, highly improbable that such a loophole could apply to our universe (indeed, Alan Guth stated in 1999 that he thought the possibility was so remote as to be insignificant). Thus, this proof is still thought to be a generally valid proof of an absolute beginning of our universe (and any other inflationary universe meeting the above 5 conditions) even today.

41. What did Alan Guth's 1999 study of inflationary model universes conclude?

Answer: Essentially, after examining all known models of inflationary universes, Guth concluded that try as physicists might to find a past-eternal model of the universe, they have been unable to do so. All inflationary models can be eternal into the future, but not into the past. They must all have a beginning.

42. What is a multiverse?

Answer: A multiverse is a hypothetical configuration proposed by Andre Linde and others as a possible implication of the collapse of a false vacuum in inflationary theory. The hypothesis suggests that little "mini-universes" (bubble universes) could be generated by the collapse of the false vacuum in the super-universe (the multiverse). All the bubble universes would be unified through the space-time of the multiverse. Andre Linde thought that it might be possible for a multiverse to be past-eternal, but as will be seen below, the Borde-Vilenkin-Guth Theorem proves that it cannot be -- and that it must have a beginning. Therefore, there can only be a finite number of bubble universes in a multiverse. Please note there is no observational evidence for a multiverse. It is purely speculative. Furthermore, it is doubtful that we will ever be able to get observational evidence of a multiverse, because we cannot get beyond our universe to obtain evidence of it.

43. What is a bouncing universe?

Answer: The bouncing universe (sometimes called "the oscillating universe") is a hypothesis that has been proposed since the time of the "Big Bang" theory. It holds that our universe is in a state of expansion, then contraction, then re-expansion, and then re-contraction. By proposing this theory, it was thought that a beginning of the universe at the Big Bang could be avoided because there could be (hypothetically) multiple "Big Bangs" -- one after every collapse at the moment of re-expansion. This could hypothetically have gone on eternally into the past.

This hypothesis has never been observationally verified and its past-eternal implications have always fallen prey to problems. Richard Tolman discovered the first problem in 1937. He showed that every expansion would necessarily increase the background radiation in the universe (which never goes away and accumulates throughout each cycle). This leads to an increase in pressure in each additional cycle which means that the universe must get bigger (before each collapse) and it must take a longer time to get to its maximum volume (before each collapse). If the universe has a finite volume today, and we go back into the past through previous cycles, those cycles would have to have been smaller and smaller. Eventually, we would have to reach a minimally small cycle with a minimum time of that cycle (the Planck length and time) which would constitute a beginning of the cycle. What Tolman showed was that even if a bouncing universe did exist, it, too, would have to have a beginning.

The theory of entropy (see below) also shows that bouncing universes could not be past eternal. Essentially, entropy means that our universe is irreversibly moving from ordered systems to disordered systems of energy, and that eventually, all systems of energy will become maximally disordered (what is called "maximum entropy"). This condition means that the universe as a whole would be at thermodynamic equilibrium (like the cosmic microwave background radiation -- incapable of doing anything) if the universe were eternal into the past. But in point of fact, our universe is not anywhere near maximum entropy; it has very low entropy (with a considerable amount of ordered systems of energy -- such as stars). This indicates that our universe was very probably not past eternal, and furthermore, very probably did not bounce even once (see the Roger Penrose number below -- the improbability of fine tuning our universe even more than it already was at the "Big Bang" is simply astounding. It is highly, highly, highly improbable).

The final two blows to the bouncing universe theory as a hypothesis allowing for a past-eternal universe have come more recently. First, the discovery of dark energy (the field attaching itself to the space-time continuum which causes it to stretch and expand) suggests strongly that the universe could never have collapsed because dark energy is much greater than the combination of visible matter and dark matter (72.4% dark energy vs. 27.6% visible matter and dark matter). How could the universe collapse? The only way would have been for the dark energy to somehow disappear, which is not physically realistic. Secondly, the B-V-G Theorem shows that even bouncing universes in higher dimensions have to have a beginning (see below).

Thus, it is highly doubtful that even if there was a bouncing universe (which the presence of an abundance of dark energy militates against), it would not have been past eternal. It would have to have had a beginning.

Quantum cosmology (question #38) allows for the possibility of another kind of bouncing universe in higher dimensional space. Einstein's theory of gravity integrated with quantum mechanics in a mathematically consistent manner (unified with the other forces of nature) called superstring theory requires that there be several "extra" space dimensions. In one class of higher-dimensional scenarios, our four-dimensional universe can be viewed as one "membrane" (called "brane" for short in the technical literature) moving around within a higher-dimensional spacetime, where there may be other branes. In the so-called "ekpyrotic" scenario of Steinhardt and Turok, our universe is one of two such branes that are parallel to each other and repeatedly collide, move apart, and collide again. The Big Bang is supposed to have been one of these collisions. They have suggested that this cycle of collisions may have been going on forever. However, as Borde, Vilenkin, and Guth make clear in their 2003 article, even bouncing universes in higher dimensional space must have a beginning (because the *average* Hubble expansion is greater than zero). See below questions #44 & 45.

44. What is the major premise of the 2003 BVG Theorem?

Answer: If any universe, multiverse, or bouncing universe has an average Hubble expansion > 0, then that universe must have a limit to its past time (a beginning). "Average Hubble expansion" means "Rate of expansion of a universe as a whole", thus, we could translate the major premise as: "If the average rate of expansion of any universe (or multiverse) is > 0, then that universe (or multiverse) would have to have a beginning".

The word "average" refers to bouncing universes, and it means that if the "average" of expansions and contractions is positive (greater than zero) then that bouncing universe would also have to have a beginning (even if the bouncing occurred through the higher dimensional space of string theory).

45. How does the major premise of the BVG Theorem work?

Please note, for those taking the college class for credit, students do not need to understand the whole answer given below to pass the exam. All that is required of the students is to know:

(i) *That all relative velocities of objects in intergalactic space will slow down into the future; therefore they must have been going faster in the past.*

(ii) *At some finite time in the past, relative velocities would have reached the speed of light, and this would have to mark a beginning of time and the universe as we know it.*

(iii) *If a higher velocity than the speed of light is discovered* in our universe, this will not undermine the proof, because it does not matter what the highest velocity is, but only that there must be a maximum velocity (whatever it may be).

(iv) There must always be a maximum possible velocity in any universe or multiverse, because if there were not, physical energy could travel at an infinite velocity, meaning that it would be everywhere at the same time. This creates a problem of multiple manifestations of energy and a series of intrinsic contradictions.

(v) Therefore, there must be a beginning of every universe or multiverse which has an average rate of expansion greater than zero.

A fuller explanation is provided below for students who are interested in why the BVG theorem works and why it is so vastly applicable to all universes and multiverses with an average rate of expansion greater than zero.

The fuller answer can be set out in four steps:

(a) First step: recall the insight of Fr. Georges Lemaitre given above – that the farther a galaxy is from our galaxy, the greater will be its recessional velocity (its speed going away from me). Assuming that the universe expanded much like a balloon being blown up, the high velocities of extra-galactic nebulae can be explained with almost perfect mathematical accuracy. If space is stretching (growing), like the elastic of a balloon being blown up, then the further a galaxy is from us (the observer), the greater its recessional velocity must be. Why? Because galaxies are not simply moving away from each other in a fixed amount of space; the space between the galaxies is actually stretching and growing (like the balloon). Thus, the more space there is between my galaxy and another galaxy, the more space there is to stretch and grow, and so we would expect that there would be more growing of space between our galaxy and a far distant galaxy than one which is closer to us (because there is more space growing). This should increase the recessional velocity in proportion to a galaxy's distance from our galaxy. Hubble had a precise equation to calculate this -- $v = H_0 D$, (where v is the recessional velocity of a distant galaxy, D is the proper distance of that galaxy from our galaxy, and H is the Hubble constant which transforms proper distance into recessional velocity). Today the Hubble constant is thought to be 69.32 ± 0.80 (km/s)/ Mpc – (kilometer per second) per megaparsec[11]. We can illustrate this very simply with a rubber band. Take out a rubber band and put it next to a ruler. Now draw a dot on the rubber band at point zero; another dot at one inch; and yet another dot at two inches. Now, take the rubber band and hold it with your left hand at point zero. With your right hand stretch the rubber band so that the dot that was at two inches is now at four inches. Evidently the dot which was at two inches from origin has expanded another two inches (to the four inch mark). But notice that the dot which was at the one inch mark has only moved to the two inch mark (an expansion of only one inch). Thus, if space as a whole is growing like a balloon (or like our rubber band), the further away a galaxy is from our galaxy (at point zero on the ruler), the more it expands per unit time. Since expansion per unit time is recessional velocity, Lemaitre is right – the further away the galaxy is, the greater its recessional velocity.

(b) Second step: There are two ways of having greater distance between our galaxy and other distant galaxies. The first way is the one described above (where galaxy #2 happens to be further away than galaxy #1). The second way is by going into the future. Let us return to our example of the rubber band. If the universe is expanding like our rubber band, then every single moment we move into the future, the recessional velocity of distant objects will be getting greater and greater. Remember our three dots: one at point zero, one at one inch, and one at two inches. When I pulled the third dot from two inches to four inches, the second dot only went from one inch to two inches. But now that the second dot is at two inches, it will do the same thing that the third dot did previously. It will now move from two inches to four inches. Thus, as we go into the future, our recessional velocities increase, because more distance is put between us and distant objects as

---

[11] The Planck spacecraft also slightly revised the Hubble Constant. It is now thought to be 67.15 + 1.2 km/s/Mpc.

we move into the future. (Remember, the greater the distance, the greater the recessional velocity).

(c) Third step: now imagine that a rocket is moving from our galaxy to a distant galaxy. Remember that space continues to grow; therefore the recessional velocities of the distant galaxy will increase as we move into the future. Here is how Alexander Vilenkin describes it:

"Suppose, for example, that [a] space traveler has just zoomed by the earth at the speed of 100,000 kilometers per second and is now headed toward a distant galaxy, about a billion light years away. That galaxy is moving away from us at a speed of 20,000 kilometers per second, so when the space traveler catches up with it, the observers there will see him moving at 80,000 kilometers per second. [100,000 kps minus 20,000 kps]."

Remember, as we move into the future, the recessional velocity of galaxies will increase; therefore, the relative velocity of the rocket (its velocity at the origin point minus the recessional velocity of a distant galaxy) will have to slow down. Since all galaxies are expanding away from each other, all relative velocities of objects will have to get slower and slower into the future.

(d) Fourth step: what is the consequence of Step Three? If the relative velocities of all objects must be getting slower and slower into the future, they must have been faster and faster into the past. Vilenkin puts it this way:

"If the velocity of the space traveler relative to the spectators gets smaller and smaller into the future, then it follows that his velocity should get larger and larger as we follow his history into the past. In the limit, his velocity should get arbitrarily close to the speed of light."

So what is the point? It is not possible to have a relative velocity greater than the speed of light in our universe. Thus, when all relative velocities were arbitrarily close to the speed of light, then past time could not have gone back any further. It represents a beginning of the universe. What if scientists discover that there is a higher velocity than the speed of light in our universe? Does that invalidate the BVG proof? No because it does not matter what the upper limit to velocity is; all that matters is that there is an upper limit to velocity in the universe (no matter what it is).

Now there must *always* be an upper limit to velocity in any universe or multiverse – if there were not, then physical energy could travel at an infinite velocity, and if physical energy could travel at an infinite velocity, then it would be everywhere at the same time. Now if it were everywhere at the same time, we would have two irresolvable problems – first, there would be a multiplication of the same physical energy everywhere in the universe which leads to a second problem, that the same space time point would have to be occupied by contradictory forms of physical energy. The whole universe or multiverse would be filled with contradictions. Now, what does this mean? It means that there must be an upper limit to velocity in every universe or multiverse, which means, in turn, that the BVG proof must be applicable to every universe or multiverse (including bouncing universes, mega-multiverses, bouncing universes in the higher dimensional space of string theory, etc.).

There are four consequences of the Borde Vilenkin and Guth proof:

(a) It applies to all universes and multiverses (including bouncing universes in higher dimensions) that have an average rate of expansion greater than zero (no matter how small).

(b) It does not matter what the physics of a given universe or multiverse might be; so long as the average Hubble expansion is greater than zero, the B-V-G proof will be applicable, because that universe or multiverse must have an upper limit to velocity.

(c) Since there is only one condition for the proof to work (namely that the average Hubble expansion be greater than zero), and it functions independently of the physics of any given universe or multiverse, it will be very difficult to disprove.

35

(d) The consequence is that it is highly probable that there is an absolute beginning to physical reality, and this is precisely what implies a creation by some transcendent power outside of physical reality (a Creator) – (see the questions for unit 1A above).

46. **Why is it so easy to establish the minor premise of the BVG Theorem for our universe, other inflationary universes, all multiverses, and even bouncing universes in higher dimensions?**

Answer: Recall, the minor premise is: "our universe, every multiverse, and every bouncing universe (that does not begin with a contraction) has an average rate of expansion greater than zero." This is easily established in our universe because the red shifting of our galaxies shows this expansion (and the high proportion of dark energy indicates that it will continue on an accelerated basis forever).

With respect to multiverses, all multiverses must be inflationary, and inflationary conditions always have a rate of expansion greater than zero. With respect to bouncing universes, all bouncing universes which do not begin with contraction must have an *average* rate of expansion greater than zero; but if they did begin with a contraction, this would imply a first phase and a beginning.

Therefore, in virtually every scenario where our universe or any multiverse in which it might be embedded, there must be a beginning. This leads to the conclusion that there must be an absolute beginning of physical reality.

47. **If there were an absolute beginning of physical reality (our universe and any hypothetical multiverse in which it might be imbedded), what does that signify about a transcendent Creator?**

Answer: If there were an absolute beginning to physical reality, then physical reality (and physical time) would not have existed prior to that beginning. Indeed, there would be no "prior" which would entail physical time. The whole of physical reality and physical time would have been *nothing.* Now if physical reality were truly nothing, and nothing can only do nothing, then physical reality could not have moved itself from nothing to something when it was nothing. This means that something else transcending our universe had to move it from nothing to something which implies a transcendent Creator.

Quotations and References from Major Scientists

I. **Quotations**

A. **The Explanation of Arvind Borde, Alexander Vilenkin, and Alan Guth of the General Conclusion of the BVG Proof:**

> Our argument shows that null and time like geodesics are, in general, past-incomplete [requiring a boundary to past time] in inflationary models, whether or not energy conditions hold, provided only that the averaged expansion condition $H_{av} > 0$ hold along these past-directed geodesics. This is a stronger conclusion than the one arrived at in previous work in that we have shown under reasonable assumptions that almost all causal geodesics, when extended to the past of an arbitrary point, reach the boundary of the inflating region of space-time in a *finite* proper time[12].

B. **Alexander Vilenkin's Non-Mathematical Explanation of Why a Boundary to Past Time Must Always Be Reached in a Universe (or Multiverse) Having an Average Hubble Expansion Greater than Zero:**

> Suppose, for example, that [a] space traveler has just zoomed by the earth at the speed of 100,000 kilometers per second and is now headed toward a distant galaxy, about a billion light years away. That galaxy is moving away from us at a speed of 20,000 kilometers per second, so when the space traveler catches up with it, the observers there will see him moving at 80,000 kilometers per second.

> If the velocity of the space traveler relative to the spectators gets smaller and smaller into the future, then it follows that his velocity should get larger and larger as

---

[12] Borde, Guth, and Vilenkin 2003 p. 3

we follow his history into the past. In the limit, his velocity should get arbitrarily close to the speed of light[13].

C. The Explanation of Borde-Vilenkin-Guth Concerning the One and Only Condition of the BVG Proof:

We made no assumptions about the material content of the universe. We did not even assume that gravity is described by Einstein's equations. So, if Einstein's gravity requires some modification, our conclusion will still hold. The only assumption that we made was that the expansion rate of the universe never gets below some nonzero value, no matter how small. This assumption should certainly be satisfied in the inflating false vacuum. The conclusion is that past-eternal inflation without a beginning is impossible[14].

D. Lisa Grossman's Summary of Why the BVG Proof Shows a Beginning of Multiverses:

Eternal inflation is essentially an expansion of Guth's idea, and says that the universe grows at this breakneck pace forever, by constantly giving birth to smaller "bubble" universes within an ever-expanding multiverse, each of which goes through its own initial period of inflation. Crucially, some versions of eternal inflation applied to time as well as space, with the bubbles forming both backwards and forwards in time (see diagram)...But in 2003, a team including Vilenkin and Guth considered what eternal inflation would mean for the Hubble constant, which describes mathematically the expansion of the universe. They found that the equations didn't work (*Physical Review Letters, DOI,* 10.1103/physrevlett.90.151301). "You can't construct a space-time with this property," says Vilenkin. It turns out that the constant has a lower limit that prevents inflation in both time directions. "It can't possibly be eternal in the past," says Vilenkin. "There must be some kind of boundary."[15]

E. The Explanation of Borde Vilenkin and Guth for Why the BVG Proof Applies to Multiverses and to

---

[13] Vilenkin 2006 p. 173
[14] Vilenkin 2006 p.175
[15] Grossman 2012 p 2.

Cyclic Universes in the Higher Dimensional Space of String Theory:

Our argument can be straightforwardly extended to cosmology in higher dimensions. For example, [1] in the model of Ref. [19] brane worlds are created in collisions of bubbles nucleating in an inflating higher-dimensional bulk space-time. Our analysis implies that the inflating bulk cannot be past-complete [i.e. must have a boundary to past time]. [2] We finally comment on the cyclic Universe model in which a bulk of four spatial dimensions is sandwiched between two three-dimensional branes...In some versions of the cyclic model the brane space-times' are everywhere expanding, so our theorem immediately implies the existence of a past boundary at which boundary conditions must be imposed. In other versions, there are brief periods of contraction, but the net result of each cycle is an expansion....Thus, as long as $H_{av} >$ 0 for a null geodesic when averaged over one cycle, then $H_{av} > 0$ for any number of cycles, and our theorem would imply that the geodesic is incomplete [i.e. must have a boundary to past time].[16]

F. Lisa Grossman's Summary of Vilenkin's Explanation for Why the Static (Cosmic Egg) Hypothesis Must be Quantum Unstable and Must therefore have a Beginning:

Vilenkin's final strike is an attack on a third, lesser-known proposal that the cosmos existed eternally in a static state called the cosmic egg. This finally "cracked" to create the big bang, leading to the expanding universe we see today. Late last year Vilenkin and graduate student Audrey Mithani showed that the egg could not have existed forever after all, as quantum instabilities would force it to collapse after a finite amount of time (arxiv.org/abs/1110.4096). If it cracked instead, leading to the big bang, then this must have happened before it collapsed - and therefore also after a finite amount of time.[17]

---

[16] Borde, Guth, and Vilenkin 2003 p. 4.
[17] Grossman 2012 pp 2-3

G. Alexander Vilenkin's Conclusion About the Beginning of the Universe (and Physical Reality itself):

"It is said that an argument is what convinces reasonable men and a proof is what it takes to convince even an unreasonable man. With the proof now in place, cosmologists can no longer hide behind the possibility of a past-eternal universe....There is no escape, they have to face the problem of a cosmic beginning."[18]

II. References

Borde, Arvind; Guth, Alan; and Vilenkin, Alexander. 2003. "Inflationary Spacetimes are Not Past-Complete," in *Physical Review Letters* (Vol. 90, No. 15, pp. 151301-1 – 151301-4).

Craig, William, and Moreland, J.P., eds. 2009. *The Blackwell Companion to Natural Theology.* Malden, MA: Wiley-Blackwell.

Grossman, Lisa. 2012. "Why Physicists Can't Avoid a Creation Event" *New Scientist* http://www.newscientist.com/article/mg21328474.400-why-physicists-cant-avoid-a-creation-event.html.

Spitzer, Robert. 2010. *New Proofs for the Existence of God: Contributions of Contemporary Physics and Philosophy* (Grand Rapids: Eerdmans).

Vilenkin, Alexander. 2006. *Many Worlds in One: The Search for Other Universes.* (New York: Hill and Wang).

---

[18] Vilenkin 2006 p 176.

Brief Biography of Key Scientists

Dr. Arvind Borde: Dr. Arvind Borde is the Senior Professor in the Department of Mathematics at the C.W. Post Campus of Long Island University. He was Visiting Scientist at the Institute of Cosmology, Tufts University from 1993--2006. He was Visiting Scientist at the Center for Theoretical Physics at the Massachusetts Institute of Technology from 2001--2002. He was a Scholar at the Kavli Institute of Theoretical Physics at the University of California at Santa Barbara from 2007—2009. He is a co-formulator of the Borde-Vilenkin-Guth Proof for a beginning of the universe (and all multiverses).

Dr. Alexander Vilenkin: Dr. Alexander Vilenkin is Professor of Physics and Director of the Institute of Cosmology at Tufts University. A theoretical physicist who has been working in the field of cosmology for 25 years, Vilenkin has written over 150 papers and is responsible for introducing the ideas of eternal inflation... His work in cosmic strings has been pivotal.[19] He is a co-formulator of the Borde-Vilenkin-Guth Proof for a beginning of the universe (and all multiverses).

Dr. Alan Harvey Guth: Dr. Alan Harvey Guth is an American theoretical physicist and cosmologist. Guth has researched elementary particle theory (and how particle theory is applicable to the early universe). Currently serving as Victor Weisskopf, Professor of Physics at the Massachusetts Institute of Technology, he is the originator of the inflationary universe theory.... At Stanford University, Guth formally proposed the idea of cosmic inflation in 1981, the idea that the nascent universe passed through a phase of exponential expansion that was driven by a positive vacuum energy density (negative vacuum pressure). The results of the WMAP mission in 2006 made the case for cosmic inflation very compelling.[20] He is a co-formulator of the Borde-Vilenkin-Guth Proof for a beginning of the universe (and all multiverses).

---

[19] Wikipedia 2013 "Alexander Vilenkin" http://en.wikipedia.org/wikiAlexander_Vilenkin
[20] Wikipedia 2013 "Alan Guth" http://en.wikipedia.org/wiki/Alan_Guth

Evidence of a Beginning from Entropy

(In both *Science, God and Creation* and *From Nothing to Cosmos* – Episode #2)

Outline of Chapter Four Content and Power Points

Power Point #4.1

Five Steps from Entropy to a Beginning

1. Useful work must be produced by ordered physical systems (disordered or random systems can't do anything).
2. Every time work is done, a physical system moves slightly from order to disorder (it loses a little bit of it's order)
3. Disordered systems do not move back spontaneously to ordered systems (it is highly highly improbable - - like the pool table analogy); thus, entropy is irreversible.
4. If our universe is an isolated physical system and it has existed for an infinite time, it would be at maximum entropy today (maximum disorder - - incapable of doing anything).
5. But in fact, our universe has a very low entropy (e.g. stars burning).

Therefore our universe has not existed for an infinite time.

It had a beginning.

Review Questions and Answers (Chapter Four)

48. What is entropy?

Answer: The idea of "entropy" in physics is a technical concept that, basically, measures the degree of "disorder" or disorganization of a system. For purely probabilistic reasons, systems left to their own devices ("isolated systems") tend to evolve in a way that keeps the level of disorganization (entropy) constant or increases it. The entropy of an isolated system almost never decreases. Systems do not spontaneously get more organized. To make a system more organized takes something coming in from outside and expending energy. The famous Second Law of Thermodynamics says that in isolated systems, entropy always increases or stays the same, and never goes down. That is why some processes are irreversible. If a process changes the entropy, then it can only go one way --- the way that entropy (disorganization) increases. The result of the Second Law of Thermodynamics is that systems tend to "run down," "wear out," "decompose," and so on. In short, all energetic systems, if left to their own devices (isolated systems) will run down, and when they do, they will no longer be able to perform work.

49. What are the implications of the second law of thermodynamics for the beginning of the universe?

Answer: If the universe is an isolated system (and there is no energy coming into it from outside), then if the universe had no beginning (and had existed for an infinite amount of time), it should have experienced the irreversible process of progressive disordering completely. In other words, it should be completely run down. This would mean that the universe would effectively be dead – it would be like cosmic microwave background radiation at a temperature exceedingly close to zero degrees kelvin (absolute zero).

Yet this is not in fact the case. Our universe has very low entropy (instead of maximum entropy) as manifest by billions upon billions of burning stars, planets, and even life forms on this planet.

The argument for a beginning may be set out in five steps:

(a) *In order for isolated physical systems to perform work (significant physical activity – such as stars burning) they must have internal order or organization* (they cannot be completely disordered; that is they cannot be the same – and the same temperature – throughout the system).

(b) *Every time work is performed by an isolated physical system, a tiny bit of its internal order is lost* (that is, it becomes a little more disordered – its entropy increases). Note that entropy is a measure of disorder in an isolated physical system.

(c) *The process of moving from order to disorder (entropy) in isolated physical systems performing work is irreversible.* No isolated physical system will move

43

spontaneously from disorder to order over the long term. This is true for purely statistical reasons. If we consider a racked set of pool balls to be an ordered system, and we shoot a cue ball at it and it becomes disordered (randomly distributed), this should not surprise us (for purely probabilistic reasons). However, if we were to shoot the cue ball at the randomly distributed pool balls, and they spontaneously reorganized themselves into a racked configuration – spitting the cue ball out at the end – we would probably be shocked, because the probability of this occurring randomly and spontaneously is exceedingly small.

(d) *If the universe is an isolated system (which is thought to be the case in the Standard Big Bang Model), and it has been performing work (such as stars burning) for an <u>infinite</u> time, then it should have reached maximum entropy today.* This is a simple conclusion from (a), (b) & (c) above. If disorder increases whenever work is performed by isolated physical systems, and the universe is an isolated physical system which has been performing work for an infinite period of time, then it should have reached maximum entropy today – that is, it should be dead – rundown, and unable to perform any work. The entire universe would be like microwave background radiation -- very close to absolute zero degrees.

(e) *However, this is clearly not the case.* The fact is, we live in a universe that has very low entropy with billions upon billions of stars burning, planets evolving, life growing on this planet, and physicists thinking about it.

(f) *Therefore, if the universe is an isolated physical system, it seems quite likely that it has not existed for an infinite amount of time – that is, it had a beginning.*

Notice that this evidence for a beginning is based on different data than the Borde-Vilenkin-Guth Proof implying that the two evidence sets mutually corroborate each other.

If we are going to negate this evidence for a beginning from entropy, we will have to show that either the universe is not an isolated system, or that we can re-start entropy at some point in our universe (like at a bounce). There is currently no evidence that the universe is not an isolated system. The bouncing hypothesis is taken up in the next question.

50. How does entropy affect the bouncing universe hypothesis?

Answer: Entropy militates against a bouncing universe for one major reason. Recall what was said about ordered systems (low entropy) being very improbable. Roger Penrose calculated the odds against low entropy at the beginning of our universe. He calculated it to be $_{10}10^{123}$ to 1 against our low entropy. This number is so enormous that if every zero were ten-point type, our solar system could not hold it. It is like the odds of a monkey typing the works of Shakespeare by random tapping of the keys in two weeks – exceedingly, exceedingly improbable. When the universe expands, its entropy increases, and if it were to contract, its entropy would increase significantly as well (Jacob Beckenstein indicated that it would be by a factor of 10^{80}). This means that the odds against low entropy at that previous cycle would have to be even greater than the odds against low entropy at our Big Bang (the entropy of the previous cycle plus the odds against low entropy in our cycle). If there were even more previous bounces, the odds against them having low entropy would be still greater. For this reason, even naturalistic physicists do not believe that the universe bounced even once.

51. Does dark energy militate against a bouncing universe?

Answer: Recall that dark energy is not like dark matter or visible matter. Dark energy interacts with the space-time field in a repulsive way (whereas dark matter and visible matter interact with the space-time field in an attractive way). This means that a prevalence of dark energy in our universe (72.6%) will produce an accelerated stretching or growing of the space-time field indefinitely. So we can be quite certain that our universe will not contract. It has only expanded since the Big Bang. So, could there have been a cycle (bounce) prior to the Big Bang? The only way there could have been a previous cycle is if this prevalence of dark energy did not exist in the previous cycle. But how could the dark energy from this cycle occur if it were not present in the previous cycle? Spontaneous creation? This does not seem very probable.

52. Does entropy provide evidence against an eternally bouncing universe?

Answer: Yes, Richard Tolman's proof does this. He noticed that every time the universe expands and collapses (a cycle), the amount of the cosmic microwave background radiation increases. Now cosmic microwave background radiation continues to endure (and accumulate) from cycle to cycle. Now the accumulation of cosmic microwave background radiation from cycle to cycle will increase the volume and duration of the cycle. We know that the time from the Big Bang to the present is 13.8 billion years (a finite expansion). Now here is Tolman's insight – if we go backwards through previous cycles, each of those cycles must have been smaller in volume and duration, and as we continue to go backwards, it will get smaller than the Planck minimum of space and time, and this would imply a beginning.

53. Summary question – How does entropy indicate a beginning of the universe?

Answer: This can be answered in three parts:

(i)   If the universe is an isolated system, and entropy cannot reset itself by pure chance, then if the universe did not have a beginning (existed for an infinite amount of time), then it would be completely run down – incapable of any activity. But this is not the case. Our universe has very low entropy, indicating that it had a beginning.

(ii) The Penrose Number indicating the odds against low entropy at the Big Bang ($_{10}10^{123}$ to 1 against) makes it exceedingly improbable that there was a previous bounce or cycle. This means that our universe has only been expanding for 13.8 billion years and would appear to have a beginning.

(iii) Richard Tolman's proof indicates that the accumulation of microwave background radiation will produce larger cycles. If we go backwards, through those hypothetical larger cycles, from our current expansion (with a duration of 13.8 billion years) we will eventually have to reach a smallest possible cycle in a finite time, implying a beginning.

Quotations and References from Major Scientists

I. **Quotations**

A. **Robert Spitzer's Summary of Implications of Entropy for the End and Beginning of the Universe in the Standard Big Bang Model:**

Entropy has significant implications for cosmology. In the standard Big Bang model, entropy predicts a universal heat death (a point at which the universe has "run down" to a state of no thermodynamic free energy to sustain motion − a point at which it has reached maximum entropy). According to the *standard* Big-Bang model, the finite observable universe is considered an isolated system, the total entropy of which is constantly increasing. If the universe lasts for a sufficient time, it will asymptotically approach a state where all energy is evenly distributed. This means that the universe will eventually reach a point at which all its energy ends up as a homogeneous distribution of thermal energy, so that no more work can be extracted from any source....Entropy in the standard big bang model, not only predicts the heat *death* of the universe, but also a beginning of the universe at some finite proper time, because if the universe had existed for an infinite amount of time, it would have already reached a state of maximum entropy (thermodynamic equilibrium). However, in fact, the entropy in the universe is quite low, indicating that it has not existed for an infinite amount of time (and therefore had a beginning).

B. **Lisa Grossman's Summary of Alexander Vilenkin's Critique of the Bouncing (Cyclic) Universe on the Basis of Entropy and The B-V-G Proof:**

Another option is a cyclic universe, in which the big bang is not really the beginning but more of a bounce back following a previous collapsed universe. The universe goes through infinite cycles of big bangs and crunches with no specific beginning. Cyclic universes have an "irresistible poetic charm and bring to mind the Phoenix", says Vilenkin, quoting Georges Lemaître, an astronomer who died in 1966. Yet when he looked at what this would mean for the universe's disorder [entropy], again the figures didn't add up. ...Disorder [entropy] increases with time. So following each cycle, the universe must get more and more disordered. But if there has already been an infinite number of cycles, the universe we inhabit now should be in a state of maximum disorder [maximum entropy]. Such a universe would be uniformly lukewarm and featureless, and definitely lacking such complicated beings as stars, planets and physicists - nothing like the one we see around us.... One way around that is to propose that the universe just gets bigger with every cycle. Then the amount of disorder [entropy] per volume doesn't increase, so needn't reach the maximum. But Vilenkin found that this scenario falls prey to the same mathematical argument as eternal inflation: if your universe keeps getting bigger, it must have started somewhere.[21]

C. **Quentin Smith's Summary of Richard Tolman's Refutation of an Infinite Bouncing Universe:**

Radiation from previous cycles accumulates in each new cycle, and the accompanying increase in pressure causes the new cycle to be longer than the last one; the universe expands to a greater radius and takes a longer time to complete the cycle. This disallows an infinite regress into the past, for a regress will eventually arrive at a cycle that is infinitely short and a radius that is infinitely small; this cycle, or the beginning of some cycle with values approaching the values of this cycle, will count as the beginning of the oscillating universe.[22]

D. **Thomas Banks' Critique of Bouncing (Cyclic) Cosmologies on the Basis of a High probability of a "black crunch" (maximum entropy at the end of a universal collapse):**

The collapsing phase of these models always have a time dependent Hamiltonian for the quantum field fluctuations around the classical background. Furthermore the classical background are becoming

---

[21] Lisa Grossman 2012 p 1.
[22] Smith 1993(a), p. 112.

singular. This means that the field theories will be excited to higher and higher energy states... High energy states in field theory have the ergodic property -- they thermalize rapidly, in the sense that the system explores all of its states. Willy Fischler and I proposed that in this situation you would again tend to maximize the entropy. We called this a Black Crunch and suggested the equation of state of matter would again tend toward p = p. It seems silly to imagine that, even if this is followed by a re-expansion, that one would start that expansion with a low entropy initial state, or that one had any control over the initial state at all.[23]

E. Sean Carroll's Refutation of all Bouncing Universes Based on the Fine-tuning Requirements of Low Entropy at the Big Bang:

Bojowald uses some ideas from loop quantum gravity to try to resolve the initial singularity and follow the quantum state of the universe past the Bang back into a pre-existing universe. If you try to invent a cosmology in which you straightforwardly replace the singular Big Bang by a smooth Big Bounce continuation into a previous spacetime, you have one of two choices: either the entropy continues to decrease as we travel backwards in time through the Bang, or it changes direction and begins to increase. Sadly, neither makes any sense. If you are imagining that the arrow of time is continuous as you travel back through the Bounce, then you are positing a very strange universe indeed on the other side. It's one in which the infinite past has an extremely tiny entropy, which increases only very slightly as the universe collapses, so that it can come out the other side in our observed low-entropy state. That requires the state at t=-infinity state of the universe to be infinitely finely tuned, for no apparent reason (the same holds true for the Steinhardt-Turok cyclic universe). On the other hand, if you imagine that the arrow of time reverses direction at the Bounce, you've moved your extremely-finely-tuned-for-no-good-reason condition to the Bounce itself. In models where

---

[23] Thomas Banks personal communication to James Sinclair on October 12, 2007 reported in Craig and Sinclair 2010 pg.

the Big Bang is really the beginning of the universe, one could in principle imagine that some unknown law of physics makes the boundary conditions there very special, and explains the low entropy (a possibility that Roger Penrose, for example, has taken seriously). But if it's not a boundary, why are the conditions there so special?[24]

II. References

Banks, Thomas, and Fischler, Willy. 2002. "Black Crunch." http://arXiv.org/abs/hep-th/0212113v.

Carroll, Sean. 2007. "Against a Bounce." www.discovermagazine.com/cosmicvariance 2007/07/02/ Against-Bounce.

Craig and Sinclair Blackwell Companion to Natural theology.

Craig, William, and Moreland, J.P., eds. 2009. *The Blackwell Companion to Natural Theology.* Malden, MA: Wiley-Blackwell.

Craig, William, and Smith, Quentin. 1993. *Theism, Atheism, and Big Bang Cosmology* (New York: Oxford University Press).

Grossman, Lisa. 2012. "Why Physicists Can't Avoid a Creation Event" *New Scientist* http://www.newscientist.com/article/mg21328474.400-why-physicists-can't-avoid-a-creation-event.html.

Smith, Quentin. 1993(a). "The Uncaused Beginning of the Universe." *In Theism, Atheism, and Big Bang Cosmology.* (New York: Clarendon Press), pp. 108-139.

Spitzer, Robert. 2010. *New Proofs for the Existence of God: Contributions of Contemporary Physics and Philosophy* (Grand Rapids: Eerdmans).

---

[24] Sean Carroll 2007. www.discovermagazine.com/cosmicvariance/2007/07/02/against-Bounce

Brief Biographies of Key Scientists

Dr. Richard Tolman: Richard Chace Tolman was an American mathematical physicist and physical chemist who was an authority on statistical mechanics. He also made important contributions to theoretical cosmology in the years soon after Einstein's discovery of general relativity. He was a professor of physical chemistry and mathematical physics at the California Institute of Technology.[25] He is well known for his proof against an eternal bouncing universe.

Dr. Roger Penrose: Sir Roger Penrose OM, FRS, is an English mathematical physicist, mathematician and philosopher. He is the Emeritus Rouse Ball Professor of Mathematics at the Mathematical Institute of the University of Oxford, as well as an Emeritus Fellow of Wadham College.

Penrose is internationally renowned for his scientific work in mathematical physics, in particular for his contributions to general relativity and cosmology. He has received a number of prizes and awards, including the 1988 Wolf Prize for physics, which he shared with Stephen Hawking for their contribution to our understanding of the universe.[26] He is also known for his calculation of the enormous odds against the low entropy of our universe at the Big Bang.

Dr. Thomas Banks: Dr. Thomas Banks is a theoretical physicist at University of California, Santa Cruz and a professor at Rutgers University. His work centers around string theory and its applications to high energy particle physics and cosmology. He was several times a visiting scholar at the Institute for Advanced Study in Princeton. Along with Fischler, Shenker, and Susskind, he is one of the four originators of M(atrix) theory, or BFSS Matrix Theory, an attempt to formulate M theory in a nonperturbative manner.[27] He and Willy Fischler formulated the theory of the "black crunch" indicating the unlikelihood of a single "bounce" of the universe.

[25] Wikipedia 2013 "Richard Tolman" http://en.wikipedia.org/wiki/Richard_C._Tolman
[26] Wikipedia 2013 "Roger Penrose" http://en.wikipedia.org/wiki/Roger_Penrose
[27] Wikipedia 2013 "Tom Banks" http://en.wikipedia.org/wiki/Tom_Banks

Fine-tuning of Universal Constants and Supernatural Design

(In both *Science, God and Creation* and *From Nothing to Cosmos* – Episodes #2&3)

Outline of Chapter Five Content and Power Points

Power Point #5.1

Anthropic Coincidences

Definition

"Anthropic Coincidence" - - A highly, highly improbable condition of the universe necessary for the origination and development of life forms.

Power Point #5.2

Anthropic Coincidences – Improbability of Low Entropy
Roger Penrose – low entropy at the BIG BANG is *highly*
improbable $10^{10^{123}}$ to 1 <u>against</u>

More zeroes than our solar system can hold!

Power Point #5.3

UNIVERSAL CONSTANTS

Definition

"Universal Constant"—A fixed number representing a limit or parameter that controls the equations of physics and the laws of nature.

Example (c= 300,000 km/s)

Power Point #5.4

Two Step Argument for Possibility of Supernatural Design

1. The values of the constants and the entropy of the universe could have been almost anything at the Big Bang.
2. Yet the range of possible anthropic values (which can give rise to life forms) is very very small (our universe's 20 constants fall exactly within this very narrow range).

Therefore the probability of having universal conditions which will permit life is exceedingly, exceedingly small - - that is, *highly highly* improbable. If no natural cause can be found to explain this, then supernatural design is highly probable.

Power Point #5.5
Three Anthropic Coincidences

1. If gravitational constant or weak force constant varied by only one part in 10^{50} (.00000000000000000000000000000000000000000000000001) higher or lower, then either the universes expansion is continually explosive or universe becomes a black hole.
2. If Mass of Proton, Mass of Electron, Electromagnetic Charge, or Gravitational Constant varied ever so slightly from their actual values, then every star in our universe would be either a blue giant (incineration of everything) or a red dwarf (everything would be frozen).
3. If Strong Nuclear Force Coupling Constant were 2% higher, then there would be no hydrogen. If 2% lower, then no element heavier than hydrogen.

Power Point #5.6

TWO PROBLEMS WITH THE MULTIVERSE HYPOTHESIS

1. **Violation of Ockham's Razor.**

2. **Fine-tuning of multiverse may be just as improbable as fine-tuning of our universe (we only moved the fine-tuning problem back one step).**

Review Questions and Answers (Chapter Five)

54. What is a universal constant?

Answer: A constant is a fixed number which is everywhere and at every time the same throughout the history of the universe. These constants control the equations of physics (which describe the laws of nature). Therefore, the constants control the laws of physics in the universe.

55. What are some examples of universal constants?

Answer: At present there appear to be about twenty universal constants – such as the speed of light constant ($c = 186,200$ miles per second) representing the maximum possible velocity in the universe. Hubble's constant ($H = 69.32 \pm 0.80$ (km/s)/Mpc – (kilometer per second) per megaparsec – this is subject to revision depending upon measurement techniques). Planck's constant and the cosmological constant are also well known. Each of the four forces in our universe has a constant or constants associated with it. The electromagnetic force has three constants: the mass of the proton, the mass of the electron, the electromagnetic charge; the strong nuclear force has the strong nuclear force coupling constant; the weak force constant, and the gravitational force, the gravitational constant – and so on.

56. How do these constants indicate a possibility of supernatural design?

Answer: This answer can be broken down into five steps:

(i) The values of the constants could have been almost anything (higher or lower) at the Big Bang if they were not set by some transcendent power.

(ii) Yet if these constants varied ever so slightly from their values (either higher or lower), the universe would not have been able to sustain any life force whatsoever -- life would not have been possible in our universe.

(iii) It seems exceedingly, exceedingly unlikely that our constants could have obtained the precise values they needed to have (for any life form to develop) when they could have had virtually any value at the Big Bang.

(iv) Therefore, pure chance cannot explain how our constants obtained anthropic values (values permitting the development of a life form). If a multiverse cannot explain this fine-tuning, then supernatural design may be indicated.

57. Give some examples of how slight variations in the values of our constants would make the universe uninhabitable by any life form. Three examples:

(i) If the gravitational constant or the weak force constant had varied from their values, by only one part in 10^{50} (.0 0000000000000000000000000000000000000000000 0000000000000000000000000001) higher or lower, the universe would have either continuously exploded in its expansion, or contracted into a black hole (where the entire mass-energy of the universe would collapse into 10^{-33} cm). Either scenario would have been disastrous for the development of any life form.

(ii) If the strong nuclear force coupling constant had been two percent higher than its value, there would be no hydrogen in our universe (no nuclear fuel for stars, no water, etc.). Conversely if the strong nuclear force coupling constant had been two percent lower than its value, there would be no element heavier than hydrogen (equally disastrous for life forms – no carbon).

(iii) If the gravitational force, the mass of the proton, the mass of the electron, or the electromagnetic charge had varied ever so slightly from their values (higher or lower), then the entire universe would have been populated by blue giant stars or red dwarf stars. Blue giants incinerate everything and red dwarfs do not give off enough heat to get beyond freezing. The precursors to life forms would have either burned up or frozen.

58. Are there other examples of anthropic conditions at the Big Bang beyond the universal constants?

Answer: Yes, recall the Penrose Number indicating the exceedingly exceedingly low probability of low entropy occurring at the Big Bang by pure chance ($_{10}10^{123}$ to 1 against low entropy). Note that low entropy is a necessary condition for the development of a life form because if entropy is too high there will not be enough useful energy to sustain and develop the universe over the course of the evolution of life.

59. Is a one-off pure chance explanation of the values of the constants realistic?

Answer: No, when one considers the stupendous odds against both the universal constants and low entropy, it does not seem any more probable for the universe to have been anthropic (capable of sustaining a life form) than for a monkey to type the works of Shakespeare by random tapping of the keys on one try. Most physicists, even unbelievers, subscribe to this. For this reason, there must be some other explanation – a metaphysical explanation (beyond our universe) that can explain it. There are two major metaphysical hypotheses proposed today – a multiverse, and supernatural intelligent design.

60. What are the weaknesses of the multiverse hypothesis in explaining the anthropic values of the constants in our universe?

Answer: There are three basic weaknesses:
(i) It is a violation of the canon of parsimony (Ockham's Razor) to postulate trillions upon trillions upon trillions of bubble universes just to explain one. This is like bringing "excess baggage" to cosmic extremes. This does not prove that the multiverse is not the explanation for our anthropic constants; it only shows that the multiverse goes against the usual propensity of nature (elegant instead of bloated to excess).
(ii) Every multiverse needs a beginning. According to the BVG Theorem, any universe or multiverse with an average expansion greater than zero, must have a beginning. Now if the multiverse must have a beginning,

then it could not have generated an infinite number of bubble universes, but only a finite number. This does not prove that the multiverse isn't responsible for our universal constants; it only narrows the range of opportunities for it to do so.

(iii) The multiverse must also be fine-tuned in its initial conditions. If a hypothetical multiverse is not fine-tuned in its initial conditions, and the emergent bubble universes will bump into each other – literally shaking the space-time continuum of the whole bubble universe, this would produce chaos both inside and outside each bubble universe making the development of life forms exceedingly difficult. Now if the multiverse must itself be fine-tuned, and it cannot be a complete explanation of the fine-tuning of our universal constants. It only moves the fine-tuning paradox back one step (to the multiverse).

61. How do the three sources of evidence for creation corroborate one another?

Answer: This can be shown in two ways:
(i) The evidence from space-time geometry proofs and from entropy (two different data sets) corroborates a beginning of the universe, and in the case of the BVG Proof, an absolute beginning of physical reality itself.

(ii) The two sources of evidence for a beginning of the universe (and physical reality) indicate a creation event by a transcendent power outside of physical reality. This corroborates well with the evidence of supernatural intelligent design of the anthropic constants and initial conditions of our universe. A transcendent Creator and an intelligent designer are complementary expressions of a similar supernatural reality.

Quotations and References from Major Scientists

I. **Quotations**

    A. **Roger Penrose's Calculation of the Improbability of our Universe's Low Entropy at the Big Bang:**

How big was the original phase-space volume **W** that the Creator had to aim for in order to provide a universe compatible with the second law of thermodynamics and with what we now observe? It does not much matter whether we take the value $W = 10^{10^{101}}$ or $W = 10^{10^{88}}$, given by the galactic black holes or by the background radiation, respectively, or a much smaller (and, in fact, more appropriate) figure which would have been the *actual* figure at the big bang. Either way, the ratio of **V** to **W** will be closely $V/W = 10^{10^{123}}$. (Try it: $10^{10^{123}} \div 10^{10^{101}} = 10 \, (10^{123} - 10^{101}) = 10^{10^{123}}$ very closely.)

This now tells us how precise the Creator's aim must have been: namely to an accuracy of one part in $10^{10^{123}}$.[28]

    B. **Davies' Calculation of the Values of the Gravitational Constant and Weak Force Constant Necessary for the Emergence of Any Life Form within the Universe:**

If G [the gravitational constant], or g_w [the weak force constant] differed from their actual values by even *one part in 10^{50}*, the precise balance against Λ_{bare} would be upset, and the structure of the universe would be drastically altered.[29] ...[I]f Λ were several orders of magnitude greater, the expansion of the universe would be explosive, and it is doubtful if galaxies could ever have formed against such a disruptive force. If Λ were negative, the explosion would be replaced by a catastrophic collapse of the universe. It is truly extraordinary that such dramatic effects would result from changes in the strength of either gravity, or the weak force, of less than one part in 10^{50}.[30]

---

[28] Penrose 1989(a), pp. 343-344.

[29] Davies 1982, p. 107. Italics mine.

[30] Davies 1982, p.108.

C. **Walter Bradley's Summary of Brandon Carter's Research on the Very Restricted Range for the Strong Nuclear Force Constant Allowing for the Emergence of Life from our Periodic Table:**

Brandon Carter in 1970 showed that a 2 percent reduction in the strong force and its associated constant would preclude the formation of nuclei with larger numbers of protons, making the formation of elements heavier than hydrogen impossible. On the other hand, if the strong force and associated constant were just 2 percent greater than it is, then all hydrogen would be converted to helium and heavier elements from the beginning, leaving the universe no water and no long-term fuel for the stars. The absolute value of the strong force constant, and more importantly, its value relative to the electromagnetic force constant is not "prescribed" by any physical theories, but it is certainly a critical *requirement* for a universe suitable for life.[31]

D. **Paul Davies' Summary of the Narrow Range of Possible Values for the Gravitational Constant, Electromagnetic Charge, Mass of the Proton, and Mass of the Electron to give Rise to Stable Stars (like our Sun) instead of Unstable Ones (like Blue Giants or Red Dwarfs) which would disallow the emergence of Life Forms:**

What is remarkable is that this typical mass M^* just happens to lie in the narrow range between the blue giants and red dwarfs. This circumstance is in turn a consequence of an apparently accidental relation between the relative strengths of gravity and electromagnetism, as will be shown. ...The product of the penetration and Maxwell-Boltzmann factors peaks around $E = (bkT)^{2/3}$. It follows that the protons that are most effective in nuclear burning are those with energy close to this value. Prolific reactions will occur if this optimum value is not far from the average value; say $kT_c \sim 10^{-2}b^2 = 10^{-2}m_p e^4/16\pi^2\varepsilon^2\hbar^2$. The temperature need not rise far above this to maintain a good supply of energy.

---

[31] Bradley 1998, p. 39. Italics mine. See also Breuer 1991, p. 183.

For the star to avoid convective instability, kT_s must exceed the ionization energy $\sim 0.1e^4 m_e/16\pi^2\varepsilon^2\hbar^2$, so...
$k^4 T_s^4 \sim 10^{-4} m_p^3 m_e^2 e^4 G^{1/2} c^{11/2} / 16\pi^2\varepsilon^2\hbar^{5/2} / 10^{-4} e^{16} m e^4 / (4\pi\varepsilon)^8\hbar^8$, which reduces to $\alpha_G / \alpha^{12}(m_e/m_p)^4$, where α is the electromagnetic fine structure constant. This remarkable relation compares the strength of gravity (on the left) with the strength of electromagnetism, and the ratio of electron to proton mass. Moreover, α is raised to the twelfth power, so the inequality is very sensitive to the value of e.[32] .....Putting in the numbers, one obtains 5.9×10^{-39} for the left hand, and 2.0×10^{-39} for the right hand side. Nature has evidently picked the values of the fundamental constants in such a way that typical stars lie very close indeed to the boundary of convective instability. The fact that the two sides of the inequality are such enormous numbers, and yet lie so close to one another [10^{-39}], *is truly astonishing.* If gravity were *very* slightly weaker, or electromagnetism *very* slightly stronger, (or the electron slightly less massive relative to the proton), all stars would be *red dwarfs.* A correspondingly tiny change the other way and they would all be *blue giants.*[33]

E. Owen Gingerich's Explanation of the High Improbability of the Resonance Levels of Carbon, Oxygen, Helium, and Beryllium, Necessary for Carbon Atoms (the Building Blocks of Life) – this led the Famous Physicist (and Atheist) Sir Fred Hoyle to belief in a "Super Intellect" Designing the Constants of Physics:

...here the internal details of the carbon nucleus become interesting: it turns out that there is precisely the right resonance within the carbon to help this process along. ...The specific resonances within atomic nuclei are something like [a sound wave which can shatter a glass at a very precise frequency], except in this case the particular energy enables the parts to stick together rather than to fly apart. In the carbon atom, the resonance just happens to match the combined energy of the beryllium atom and a colliding

---

[32] Davies 1982, p. 71-73.
[33] Davies 1982, p. 71-73. Italics mine.

helium nucleus. Without it, there would be relatively few carbon atoms. Similarly, the internal details of the oxygen nucleus play a critical role. Oxygen can be formed by combining helium and carbon nuclei, but the corresponding resonance level in the oxygen nucleus is half a percent too low for the combination to stay together easily. Had the resonance level in the carbon been 4 percent lower, there would be essentially no carbon. Had that level in the oxygen been only half a percent higher, virtually all of the carbon would have been converted to oxygen. Without that carbon abundance, none of us would be here now.

I am told that Fred Hoyle, who together with William Fowler first noticed the remarkable arrangement of carbon and oxygen nuclear resonances, has said that nothing has shaken his atheism as much as this discovery. [34]

F. Fred Hoyle's Conclusion Concerning the High Improbability of a Universe Hospitable to Life – a Super Intellect:

Would you not say to yourself, "Some super-calculating intellect must have designed the properties of the carbon atom; otherwise the chance of my finding such an atom through the blind forces of nature would be utterly miniscule?" Of course you would…. A common sense interpretation of the facts suggests that a superintellect has monkeyed with physics, as well as with chemistry and biology, and that there are no blind forces worth speaking about in nature. The numbers one calculates from the facts seem to me so overwhelming as to put this conclusion almost beyond question.[35]

G. Paul Davies' Conclusion about the Fine-tuning of Universal Constants and Initial Conditions Necessary for Life – God or A Multiverse:

…the numerical coincidences [necessary for an anthropic universe] could be regarded as evidence of design. The delicate fine-tuning in the values of

---

[34] Gingerich 2000, pp. 524-25.
[35] Hoyle 1981, pp. 8-12.

the constants, necessary so that the various different branches of physics can dovetail so felicitously, might be attributed to God. It is hard to resist the impression that the present structure of the universe, apparently so sensitive to minor alterations in the numbers, has been rather carefully thought out. Such a conclusion can, of course, only be subjective. In the end it boils down to a question of belief. Is it easier to believe in a cosmic designer than the multiplicity of universes necessary for the weak anthropic principle to work? ...Perhaps future developments in science will lead to more direct evidence for other universes, but until then, the seemingly miraculous concurrence of numerical values that nature has assigned to her fundamental constants must remain the most compelling evidence for an element of cosmic design.[36]

H. Bruce Gordon's Conclusion from the Combined Evidence of the Borde-Vilenkin-Guth Proof, the Evidence of Entropy, and the Fine-Tuning of Universal Constants and Initial Conditions:

When the logical and metaphysical necessity of an efficient cause, the demonstrable absence of a material one, and the proof that there was an absolute beginning to any universe or multiverse are all conjoined with the fact that our universe exists and its conditions are fine-tuned immeasurably beyond the capacity of any mindless process, the scientific evidence points inexorably toward transcendent intelligent agency as the most plausible, if not the only reasonable explanation.[37]

---

[36] Davies 1983, p.189.
[37] Gordon, Bruce 2010 p 103.

II. References

Bradley, Walter L. 1998. "Designed or Designoid?" *Mere Creation:* Science, *Faith & Intelligent Design.* Ed. by William A. Dembski. (Downers Grove, IL: InterVarsity Press).

Carter, Brandon. 1967. "The significance of numerical coincidences in nature," http://arxiv.org/abs/0710.3543

Davies, Paul 1982. *The Accidental Universe.* (New York. Cambridge University Press). -------1983. *God and the New Physics.* (New York: Simon and Schuster).

Gingerich, Owen. 2000. "Do the Heavens Declare?" *In The Book of the Cosmos.* Ed by Dennis Richard Danielson. (Cambridge, MA Perseus Publishing).

Gordon, Bruce. 2010. Inflationary Cosmology and the String Multiverse in *New Proofs for the Existence of God: Contributions of Contemporary Physics and Philosophy* by Robert J. Spitzer, S.J., (Grand Rapids: Eerdmans Publishing).

Hoyle, Fred 1981. "The Universe: Past and Present Reflections." *Engineering and Science.* (Pasadena, CA: California Institute of Technology, November), pp. 8-12.

Penrose, Roger 1989(a). *The Emperor's New Mind.* (Oxford: Oxford University Press).

Spitzer, Robert 2010. *New Proofs for the Existence of God: Contributions of Contemporary Physics and Philosophy* (Grand Rapids: Eerdmans).

Brief Biographies of Key Scientists

Sir Fred Hoyle: Sir Fred Hoyle was an English astronomer noted primarily for his contribution to the theory of stellar nucleosynthesis and his often controversial stance on other cosmological and scientific matters—in particular his rejection of the "Big Bang" theory [he later retracted this rejection]. Hoyle spent most of his working life at the Institute of Astronomy at

Cambridge and served as its director for a number of years.[38] He was known for changing his atheistic views to a conviction about a "super calculating intellect" responsible for the constants of physics, chemistry, and biology.

Dr. Paul Davies: Dr. Paul Charles William Davies is an English physicist, writer and broadcaster, currently a professor at Arizona State University as well as the Director of BEYOND: Center for Fundamental Concepts in Science. He is also currently affiliated with the Institute for Quantum Studies at Chapman University in California. He has held previous academic appointments at the University of Cambridge, University College London, University of Newcastle upon Tyne, University of Adelaide and Macquarie University. His research interests are in the fields of cosmology, quantum field theory, and astrobiology.[39] He is known for his books on the implications of creation and design in the universe.

Dr. Brandon Carter: Dr. Brandon Carter is an Australian theoretical physicist, best known for his work on the properties of black holes and for being the first to name and employ the anthropic principle in its contemporary form. He is a researcher at the Meudon campus of the Laboratoire Univers et Theories, part of the CNRS. He studied at Cambridge under Dennis Sciama. He found the exact solution of the geodesic equations for the Kerr/Newman electrovacuum, and the maximal analytic extension of this solution. In the process, he discovered the extraordinary *fourth constant of motion* and the Killing-Yano tensor.[40] He also articulated several remarkable anthropic coincidences implying the fine-tuning of several universal constants.

Dr. Owen Gingerich: Dr. Owen Gingerich, former Research Professor of Astronomy and of the History of Science at Harvard University, is a senior astronomer emeritus at the Smithsonian Astrophysical Observatory. He has written many books on the history of astronomy,[41] and is known for his strong conviction about purpose and design in the initial conditions and constants of the universe.

---

[38] Wikipedia 2013 "Fred Hoyle" http://en.wikipedia.org/wiki/Fred_Hoyle
[39] Wikipedia 2013 "Paul Davies" http://en.wikipedia.org/wiki/Paul_Davies
[40] Wikipedia 2013 "Brandon Carter" http://en.wikipedia.org/wiki/Brandon_Carter
[41] Wikipedia 2013 "Owen Gingerich" http://en.wikipedia.org/wiki/Owen_Gingerich

Responses to Counter-positions (particularly Richard Dawkins)

(In only *From Nothing to Cosmos* – Episode #3)

Outline of Chapter Six Content and Power Points

Power Point #6.1
Is it sufficient to say that the fine-tuning of the universe is just there (needs no explanation)?

No, because every non-life alternative could have occurred at the big bang.

Imagine a black sheet the size of our Milky Way divisible into $_{10}10^{123}$ black dots.

Now imagine there is only one red dot in that whole sheet.

The possibility of a high entropy universe are all the black dots, and the possibility of a low entropy universe is the one red dot.

Throw a needle toward the black sheet from two galaxies away. The odds of getting a low entropy universe by pure chance are the same as the pin striking the one red dot amidst all the other black dots by pure chance.

Power Point #6.2
Why does a creator have to be absolutely simple?

1. A creator must be an uncaused cause (if a creator is not to need a creator, it must be completely uncaused).

2. An uncaused cause must be a pure act of existing through itself. If there is anything in it different from the pure act of existing through itself, that difference would not exist through itself, and would therefore have to be caused (created).

3. The pure act of existing through itself cannot be restricted, because any restriction to it would have to be different from it, and whatever is different from it would not be able to exist through itself, and would therefore have to be created.

4. Complexity implies parts, and parts imply restrictions. However, an uncaused cause (the pure act of existing through itself) cannot have any restrictions. Therefore an uncaused cause cannot have any complexity whatsoever.

Power Point #6.3

The pure act of existing through itself is existence itself, and can therefore cause (create) existence in any restricted way.

The pure act of existing through itself is completely self-transparent because it does not have to overcome any spatial or temporal limitations to be in touch with itself.

Therefore it can be in relation to itself in every possible way, and is therefore an unrestricted act of thinking.

The pure act of existing through itself cannot have any temporal *restriction* and would therefore be a timeless being

Summary:
The uncaused cause (the pure act of existing through itself) must at once be:
  (i)   A creator
  (ii) An unrestricted act of thinking (a self-transparent being in relation to itself in all possible ways)
  (iii) An unrestricted being that is not conditioned by space and *time*.

John Henry Newman
"Informal inference" occurs when multiple data sets (which are probable independent of one another) converge on a single conclusion.

Review Questions and Answers (Chapter Six)

62. Why is the Big Bang Significant in Arguments for a Universal Designer?

There are many intuitional approaches to supernatural design that take their evidence from the universe *after* the Big Bang. Some thinkers see the hand of God in the development of the earth itself (the privileged planet) and others see the hand of God in the movement from non-living to living beings, from non-sentient to sentient living beings, and from non-self-conscious to self-conscious beings. All of these *intuitions* may be valid, but they are not the strongest argument that can be made for people who do *not* have faith (or whose faith is relatively weak). This group will not appreciate an appeal to a supernatural cause if there is even a remote possibility of a *natural* cause. The problem of appealing to a supernatural cause for the earth's development, for example, is that there might be a series of unknown natural causes which may increase the probability of the earth's development by purely natural means. Since we do not know whether we have exhausted all natural causation, we cannot be sure that such a natural cause (or causes) does not exist. If natural cause is later discovered in an area where we attributed supernatural causation, it would undermine credibility in our argumentation.

The advantage of using design arguments that take evidence from the Big Bang is twofold:

(i)   The Big Bang is a boundary condition for natural causation. There literally is no prior natural cause at the Big Bang. The beginning of our universe's expansion is the beginning of natural causation in the universe described by the General Theory of Relativity.

(ii) The initial conditions and constants of the universe are the most fundamental building blocks of the universe. It is very difficult (if not impossible) to find a more fundamental condition than the low entropy of our universe at the Big Bang and our twenty universal constants at the Big Bang.

Because of this, it is very difficult (if not impossible) to appeal to a prior natural cause or a more fundamental physical reality to explain the occurrence of the highly highly improbable fine-tuning of the universe necessary for life forms. This makes supernatural design (an intelligent cause existing beyond our universe) a reasonable and responsible explanation – perhaps more reasonable and responsible than any natural explanation.

Since a chain is only as strong as its weakest link, we should try to construct a chain which is very strong for those whose faith is developing. We do not want to leave ourselves open to criticism when we appealed to a supernatural cause, only to find out that a natural cause is discovered a few years later. As noted earlier, I think post creation design intuitions are exceedingly edifying for believers, but they can be a "turn-off" for those whose faith is not fully developed. It is best to use the stronger arguments that speak about fundamental causes at the Big Bang.

63. Why is the Assertion, "That's just the way it was..." an Inadequate Explanation for the Fine-tuning of our Universe at the Big Bang?

Some people contend that there is no need to give an explanation for the fine-tuning of our universe, because our universe is all that there is, and it is in fact here, and there is no reason to believe that it could have been anything else. At first glance, this seems to be a reasonable statement of the facts, but in reality, it is not because there is good physical reason to believe that the universe could have been other than it is. The truth is that there is no necessity for low entropy at the Big Bang. Indeed, as we saw earlier, high entropy at the Big Bang (for purely naturalistic reasons) is far far more probable than the low entropy that occurred. This provokes an important question for physicists which cannot be ignored. Why did this highly improbable initial condition of our universe occur when simple probabilities would have dictated otherwise?

Roger Penrose puts the question in a way that is helpful. He notices that when 10^{80} baryons worth of mass-energy are coming into being, it gives rise to $_{10}10^{123}$ *equally possible* phase-space options for the entropy of our universe. Of that $_{10}10^{123}$ phase-space options, only a mere fraction of them will be low entropy options which will enable life to develop within the universe. This gives rise to the question "Why did this incredibly small phase space option occur amidst the far far greater number of phase space options ($_{10}10^{123}$) that could never have given rise to a life form?" It is not good enough to say "Just because" or "Because it did." This is tantamount to the same person winning the lottery a trillion-trillion-trillion times in a row and everybody saying "That's just the way it is, and it could not have been otherwise." One might want to ask whether the person running the lottery was related to the person winning. It would be ridiculous not to ask!

It might help to illustrate this further. Let's suppose that every phase space option that could have occurred with our mass energy (10^{80} baryons) at the Big Bang were like a huge black sheet that could extend over the size of our Milky Way Galaxy and was divisible into $_{10}10^{123}$ little pinholes. Now all these pinholes are black except for one pinhole which is red, and the red pinhole is the only low entropy phase space option that will give rise to life forms. All of the black ones will be high entropy options that will not allow for the development of life in the universe. All the black pinholes and the red pinhole could have occurred at the Big Bang. Now a pin is launched from a vantage point two galaxies away from the sheet and it tumbles toward the sheet, and hits the red pinprick straight on. Can it really be said that "That's just the way it was, and it could not have been other than it was?" This makes far less sense than saying that the person can win the lottery a trillion-trillion-trillion times in a row and it couldn't have been other than it was.

The same holds true for the values of our universal constants. The range of constants for an anthropic universe (capable of sustaining a life form) is exceedingly exceedingly small by comparison to the range of constants that will give rise to a non-anthropic universe (not capable of sustaining a life form) --given the mass energy of our universe, its four forces, and the dynamic nature of its space-time continuum. Every non-anthropic value of the constants could have occurred at the Big Bang (because there is no intrinsic bias toward the anthropic ones). Since there are so many more possibilities for non-anthropic values of constants than anthropic ones at the Big Bang, one must ask "Why did the anthropic ones occur?" "Why did we win the lottery a trillion-trillion-trillion times in a row?"

This is why the vast majority of physicists who do not want to believe in a supernatural cause have made recourse to a multiverse. Every one of these physicists recognizes (either implicitly or explicitly) that it is not good enough to say, "That's just the way it was, and it could not have been other than it was." They recognize that the universe could have been other than it was, and indeed that it would have been much much more probable to be non-anthropic than to be anthropic. For this reason, they choose a multiverse as a naturalistic explanation of our highly improbable anthropic universe.

64. What did Richard Dawkins Overlook in the Major Thesis of *The God Delusion* when he said that "A designer would always have to be more improbable

than anything it designed"?

The response to this question is given in the eight-step proof below. Please note that only Steps (1) through (3) and Step (8) are given in the DVD presentation. The full proof (including Steps (4) through (7)) may be of interest to those who are seeking the complete answer or who wish to teach or facilitate this material.

Editor's Note
You may feel a bit overwhelmed by this response to Richard Dawkins' The God Delusion (2006 Bantam Books), because it is quite metaphysical. The response covers the basic content of one-half of a collegiate level metaphysics course, and so I would not expect you to have a deep understanding of the contents. Nevertheless, I did not want to oversimplify the response to Dawkins because it is a very popular misconception in today's culture. I decided to err on the side of completeness rather than simplicity, and I hope you will be patient with this choice. In so doing, I hope that you will appreciate the richness and depth of the philosophical tradition beginning with Plato and Aristotle continuing through Augustine and Aquinas and continuing into the present with many modern philosophers cited below. I also hope that you would be able to understand the basic flow and solidity of the argument because it establishes not only the existence of an uncaused cause, but also the uniqueness, unrestricted nature, complete simplicity, transtemporality, and unrestricted intelligence of the Creator to which contemporary physics is pointing. At the same time, you will discover that Richard Dawkins has concluded to precisely the opposite conclusion that the logic and metaphysics of an uncaused cause require.

Richard Dawkins' core argument in the *God Delusion* may be summarized as follows:
1. A designer must always be more complex than what it designs.
2. Whatever is more complex is more improbable.
3. Therefore a designer will always be more improbable than what it designs.

There can be little doubt that Dawkins' second premise ("whatever is more complex is more improbable") is true, because the more complex a reality is, the more parts there are to order or organize. Since order or organization is more improbable than disorder, it follows that the more parts there are to order, the more improbable the ordering will be.

However, Dawkins' first premise is highly contestable and quite frankly, it ignores 2,400 years of philosophical history going back to Plato and Aristotle, then proceeding to Augustine and Aquinas and then to contemporary philosopher's such as Jacques Maritain, Etienne Gilson, Joseph Owens, Josef Pieper, Bernard Lonergan, Karl Rahner, and all of their followers. All of these philosophers maintain that an uncaused cause (a Creator and designer) would have to be absolutely **simple** (a complete absence of complexity) instead of more complex. Ironically, this means by Dawkins second premise ("whatever is more complex is more improbable"), the Creator or designer would have to be the most probable reality of all.

Step (1)
There Must be at Least One
Uncaused Cause in all Reality.

Aristotle first formulated this proof (as an "Unmoved Mover" Proof) in Book 8 of the *Physics* and Book 12 of the *Metaphysics*. The Proof was later expanded to the "Uncaused Cause" Proof by Thomas Aquinas and there are many versions of it today (see for example, Chapter Nineteen of Bernard Lonergan's *Insight: A Study of Human Understanding*). The essential elements of this Proof are as follows:

i. Definitions
   "Caused Cause:" A caused cause is a reality that does not exist through itself – it is dependent on causation for existence, and must therefore await causation in order to exist. Without causation, it is merely hypothetical, and literally nothing.

   Causes include constituent parts or conditions for something to exist; for example, cells are composed of proteins and amino acids, which in turn are composed of molecules, which in turn are composed of atoms, etc. This would also include necessary structures and organizing components of those constituent parts, such as the particular structures of proteins, amino acids, molecules, etc. Without these constituent parts, conditions, and organizing structures, the cell would not exist. Additionally, any element "outside" of a reality necessary for its existence would also be a cause – such as light, water, and nutriment for a cell.

"Uncaused Cause:" A reality which does not require any cause to exist. It exists purely through itself without any conditions whatsoever. As will be seen below, it must be the pure act of existing through itself.

ii.   There must exist at least one Uncaused Cause.
Basic Proof: If the whole of reality were composed only of caused causes (realities that must await causation to exist), then the whole of reality would be awaiting causation to exist because there would be no existing cause of their existence – the whole of reality would be literally nothing -- awaiting causation to exist. Therefore, there must be at least one reality that does not have to await causation to exist (which exists through itself alone) and causes the existence of realities awaiting that causation. Without this uncaused cause, the whole of reality would be literally nothing.

Further Explanation: It does not matter whether one postulates an infinite number of caused causes (realities awaiting causation to exist), because an infinite number of postulated realities awaiting causation to exist (without an existing cause) is collectively still awaiting causation to exist – it is literally an infinite amount of nothing, and an infinite amount of nothing is still nothing.

Step (2)
An Uncaused Cause must be the
Pure Act of Existing through Itself.

As seen above, there must be at least one uncaused cause – at least one reality which does not have to await causation to exist. The one thing we know about this uncaused cause is that it must exist through itself alone (otherwise it too would be awaiting causation to exist). Thus, the uncaused cause must have the power to exist through itself, and more than this, that power must be active – it must be an acting power to exist through itself alone, and so Thomas Aquinas called it "the act of existing through itself alone."

Inasmuch as an uncaused cause would have to be an act of existing through itself *alone*, it must also be the *pure* act of existing through itself. The word *"pure"* here is important because there cannot be *anything* in the "act of existing through itself" which is different from it. If there were anything other than the "act of existing through itself" in it, that part or dimension of it would *not* exist through itself, and therefore, it would have to be caused. Since an uncaused cause cannot have a part or dimension which needs to be caused, it must be a *pure* "act of existing through itself."

Step (3)
A Pure Act of Existing through Itself
must be Unrestricted.

Anything which restricts the pure act of existing through itself would have to be different from it because "what restricts" is different from what is restricted. What are these restrictions? There are three major categories of restrictions to the act of existing:

a. Restrictions as to a particular *way* of existing (such as the way of existing like an electron or a proton).
b. Temporal restrictions – which limit a reality to existing at particular times (through a temporal continuum which is divisible into earlier and later).
c. Spatial restrictions (which limits a being to existence at particular places through a spatial continuum which is divisible into "here and there").

Whatever restricts "an act of existing" must be different from it, and so there must be two dimensions to every restricted reality – the act of existing *and* the restrictions to it. There can be no reality which is restrictions alone – there must be something which is restricted. A square object is not merely the limitations of square (four equal sides and four inscribed right angles) – it is *something* (in reality or in a mind) which *has* the restrictions of "four equal sides and four inscribed right angles." An electron is not reducible to its restriction (attracting protons and repelling other electrons) – it is a *reality* which is restricted to attracting protons and repelling other electrons at particular magnitudes. Notice then that a reality is not reducible to its restriction – there must be *something* which is restricted. Notice further that these restrictions are different from the something which is restricted by them.

Now, if every restriction is *different* from the "something that it restricts," then the "*pure* act of existing through itself" cannot have any restriction in it. If it did, then these restrictions would be different from the act of existing through itself, and would therefore not exist through themselves, meaning that they would have to be caused. Therefore, the "pure act of existing through itself" cannot be restricted in any way whatsoever.

Interestingly, Stephen Hawking seems to have recognized this in his book *A Brief History of Time* when he says,

"If we discover a complete theory, it would be the ultimate triumph of human reason – for then we should know the mind of God…Even if there is only one possible unified theory, it is just a set of rules and equations. What is it that breathes fire into the equations and makes a universe for them to describe?" (Hawking 1988 p. 174).

Hawking seems to recognize that the equations of physics describe only a set of *parameters* (limits such as maximums, minimums, and ratios of interaction) describing the particular actions and interactions of physical reality in space and time. They do not explain the *existence* of these parameters. The existence of physical reality is one thing and the equations of physics which describe its parameters are something different. They are unified with each other, but they are two different dimensions of physical reality. In the language we use above, there is the dimension of the act of existing (what breathes fire into the equations of physics) and the restrictions to existence (the parameters or equations of physics).

In sum, every restriction to the act of existing through itself would have to be different from it, and would therefore not exist through itself, meaning that it would have to be caused. Since an uncaused cause cannot in any way be caused, the pure act of existing through itself must be completely unrestricted (that is, without any restriction to a particular place, time, or way of existing).

This insight coincides with the Thomistic principle that "existence must precede essence." "Existence" refers to the act of existing (like Hawking's "what breathed fire into the equations ..."). "Essence" refers to a way of existing such as the way of an electron or a proton or a cell or a person (like Hawking's equations of physics).

Now let us return to an act of existing through itself. It is clear that if an act of existing through itself had an essence other than itself – any way of acting (other than the act of existing through itself) – that essence would not exist through itself, and so it would have to be caused by "an act of existing through itself." Any restriction to an act of existing through itself would have to be different from the act of existing through itself, and therefore would also have to be caused by the pure act of existing through itself. This means that a pure act of existing through itself must be prior to any restricted way of acting, because it would have to exist in a pure state prior to causing any restricted essence whatsoever. Thus, a pure act of existing through itself must be the most fundamental state of reality, and completely unrestricted.

One last clarification. The term "unrestricted" refers to the absence of restriction within the act of existing through itself. It does not refer to an unrestricted (infinite) spatial continuum or temporal continuum, but rather to the complete absence of the spatial continuum and temporal continuum (which allow for restriction). Therefore, the act of existing through itself has no spatial restriction (and is not subject to a spatial continuum), no temporal restriction (and is not subject to a temporal continuum), and no restriction of any kind. Though it is virtually impossible to visualize what a non-spatial and non-temporal act of existence would be like, we must acknowledge that a pure act of existing through itself must be the most fundamental form of reality – because every restriction would have to be caused by it.

Step (4)
A Pure Unrestricted Act of Existing through Itself Must be Unique
(One & only one)

The Basic Proof (in three premises):
(i)   If there is to be multiplicity among realities, there must be a difference between those realities.
(ii) If there is to be differences among realities, at least one of those realities must be restricted.
(iii) But there can be no restriction in the pure act of existing through itself (from Step (3) above).
        Therefore, there cannot be more than one pure act of existing through itself *(modus tollens)*.

Explanation of the Proof:
The first premise is true a priori, because if there is no difference of any kind between two realities, they must be the self-same reality. Let us postulate two realities – X_1 and X_2. Now, let us suppose there is no difference between them – no difference as to space-time point, no difference in power or activity, no difference of qualities or characteristics, no difference whatsoever. What are they? Obviously, the same reality, and as such, there is only one.

The second premise is also true a priori. Think about it. If there is going to be a difference between say X_1 and X_2 (so there can be a multiplicity of them), then one of them will have to be something or have something or be somewhere or be in some other dimension that the other one is not. Let's suppose that X_1 has something that X_2 does not. This means that X_2 is restricted or limited because it lacks this quality or characteristic. Similarly, if one postulates that X1 is something that X_2 is not, than X_2 would again have to be limited (as manifest by its lack of that "something"). The same would hold true if X_1 was somewhere that X_2 was not, and if X_1 were in another dimension that X_2 was not. In short, every differentiating factor will entail a restriction of at least one of the differentiated realities.

The third premise has already been proved in Step (3) above ("But there can be no restriction in the pure act of existing through itself").

Let's see how this works. Let us suppose that there are two pure acts of existing, then by the first premise, there will have to be some difference between Act of Existing$_1$ and Act of Existing$_2$. Recall if there are no differences whatsoever between them, then they would be the self-same reality (one reality). Now if there is a difference between them, then one of them will have to have something, be something, be somewhere, or be in another dimension that the other one is not. If one of the pure acts of existing is restricted as to what it is (its way of existing), or where it is (its space-time point or its dimension), then it could not be unrestricted. As was shown in Step (3) above, a pure act of existing through itself must be completely unrestricted (otherwise there would be something in it that needed to be caused). This would mean that every pure act of existing$_2$ would have to have some kind of restriction, meaning that it could not be completely uncaused. This second pure act of existence therefore could not really be a *pure* act of existing through itself (a completely uncaused cause).

Therefore, there can only be one pure act of existing through itself (and only one uncaused cause).

Step (5)
The One Pure Act of Existing through Itself must be the Ultimate Cause (Creator) of all else that is.

(A) As shown above, an uncaused cause must be a pure unrestricted act of existing through itself, and there can only be one pure unrestricted act of existing through itself, meaning that there can only be one uncaused cause in all reality.

(B) If there can only be one uncaused cause in all reality, then the rest of reality must be caused (brought into existence).

(C) Therefore, the one uncaused cause must be the ultimate cause of the existence of everything in reality besides itself. This is what is meant by the term "Creator."

Step (6)
The One Unrestricted Act of Existing through Itself is Transtemporal

As we saw in Step (3) above, a pure unrestricted act of existing could not be subject to a temporal continuum because a temporal continuum would be different from it and would therefore have to be created by it. This means that the pure act of existing through itself is more fundamental than a temporal continuum, and that the temporal continuum is a creation --like a thought in the mind of a timeless and unrestricted act of mentation --see below Step (7).

We must acknowledge at the outset, that a timeless act of mentation is impossible to visualize because as Kant pointed out in the *Critique of Pure Reason*, our experience (and imagination) is conditioned by space and time. So how can we conceive of something we cannot imagine (picture think)? We can only do this by a kind of *via negativa* – that is by a conceptual process which avoids the temporalizing dimension of the imagination (picture thinking). We will have to avoid trying to "get a picture of it," and rest content with a negative judgment, namely, that there exists the pure unrestricted act of existing through itself which does *not* exist through a temporal continuum, nor through a spatial continuum, nor through anything else which is not itself. This pure act is beyond any specialized or temporalized image, and therefore beyond the universe and physical reality itself. Nothing more can be said without distorting the reality through the conditions of our spatial and temporal imagination.

Step (7)
The Pure Unrestricted Act of Existing Through Itself Is an Unrestricted Act of Mentation (Thinking)

What is thinking? A detailed explanation of this is given in my book: *New Proofs for the Existence of God: Contributions of Contemporary Physics and Philosophy* (Chapter Four). For the purposes of this *Study Guide*, a summary will be sufficient.

(A) Thinking (in contrast to imagining – or picture thinking) is the grasp of relationships among realities – qualitative relationships, causal relationships, quantitative relationships, logical relationships, temporal relationships, spatial relationships, and any other intelligible relationship responding to the questions "What?" "Where? "Why?" "How?" "How many?" and "How frequently?"

(B) The ability to grasp relationships presumes some underlying unity through which the differences among realities can be related. For example, a map can unify diverse geographical locations so that they can be seen *in relation* to one another. A clock provides a unity for different times so that they may be seen in relationship to one another. There must be some underlying unity to bring together causes and effects in causal relationships. Similarly, the same holds true for "What?" or "How?" or "How many?" etc. We might summarize by saying that thinking is a unifying act that sets differences into relationship with one another so that each aspect of the relationship can be understood through its relationship to the others.

(C) As noted above, the pure act of existing through itself has no spatial, temporal, or other intrinsic restriction. Therefore, it is completely transparent to itself – meaning that it is in relation to itself in every way – there is simply no spatial, temporal, or other restriction to prevent it. At the most fundamental level, this is thinking or intelligence – a unity among relationship. We might analogize this by our own act of self-consciousness in which the same reality is both "grasper" and "grasped". This does not imply that we are divided into parts because it is one and the same being that is grasping and is grasped in the act of self-consciousness. Nevertheless, there are distinct dimensions of the same self within the relationship. Sometimes we can be aware of ourselves being aware of ourselves. Once again, we do not break into three parts, but the one self-conscious reality has three distinct relational dimensions: the grasper, the grasped, and the grasper grasping the act of grasping.

Let us return now to the pure unrestricted act of existing. Inasmuch as it is completely self-transparent, it can be present to itself (to use a precarious spatial analogy "inside" itself), and even present to itself being present to itself ("inside itself inside itself").

Inasmuch as it is naturally self-transparent, it is naturally self-conscious. Its natural state is self-consciousness (presence to self). Embedded in this self- consciousness, is an awareness of the difference between itself as grasper, grasped, and "grasper of the grasped," and so there is not only an awareness of self, but an awareness of relational *differences* within itself. Once "self" and "difference" are grasped, all other ideas can be generated. The self can grasp not only itself, but what is different from itself – restriction and change. By grasping "self," "difference," "restriction," and "change," it can then generate the whole range of finite intelligibility.

In his remarkable work *The Sophist*, Plato shows how the entire world of intelligibility can be generated from five primary ideas ("forms"): being, similarity, difference, change ("motion"), and the unchanging ("rest"). This key insight explains how a perfectly self-conscious reality (aware of the relational differences within its self-conscious act) will naturally generate the five primary ideas of Plato, and how these, in turn can generate the entire world of finite and changeable intelligibility.

Notice that this unrestricted act of mentation is not like a brain or anything material or restricted. It is the natural state of a pure unrestricted act of existing through itself. We cannot visualize it or imagine it; we can only *understand* that it is the natural state of a pure unrestricted act of existence through itself and that the pure unrestricted act of existing through itself must exist (as the one necessary "uncaused cause"). Bernard Lonergan comes to a similar conclusion in his work *Insight: A Study of Human Understanding*, and calls the first cause "an unrestricted act of understanding understanding itself" (Chapter Nineteen – pp. 657-708 – 1992 University of Toronto Press). Inasmuch as the pure unrestricted act of existing though itself is an unrestricted act of thinking, it can design the entire world of finite being.

Step (8)
The Pure Unrestricted Act of Existing through Itself must be Absolutely Simple
(the absence of complexity).

Basic Argument:
Complexity entails parts; parts entail restriction.

But there can be no restriction in the pure act of existing through itself.

Therefore, there can be no parts and no complexity in the pure act of existing through itself.

Explanation:
The first premise will probably be evident to you. Anything which is complex must have parts constituting a greater whole. Now if there are parts constituting a greater whole, the parts must be more restricted than the whole (by definition), and therefore the parts must have restrictions

as to their time, space, or way of existing.

The proof of the second premise ("there can be no restriction in the pure act of existing through itself") was given in step (3) above.

Conclusion:
By *modus tollens*, if there can be no restrictions in the pure act of existing through itself, then there can be no parts in the pure act of existing through itself, and if no parts, then no complexity. It must be absolutely simple.

Response to Dawkins' Contention

As noted in the introduction to this Chapter, Dawkins contended that every designer would have to be more complex than what it designed, and from this he concludes that every designer must be more improbable than what it designs because more complexity is always more improbable. We now see that Dawkins has overlooked about 2,400 years of philosophical history, and failed to notice that the uncaused cause (which is the Creator and designer) must be absolutely simple (the absence of complexity). If the above reasoning is correct, then the designer would not be more complex than what it designed, but rather much less complex than what it designed, indeed, the absence of complexity.

If we combine the above conclusion with Dawkins' second premise (more complexity is more improbable) --which is certainly true, then we get the remarkable result that an uncaused cause (the presumed designer) is the most probable reality of all. If more complexity is more improbable, then the absence of complexity is the least improbable of all (the most probable of all). This is precisely the conclusion that Aristotle, Thomas Aquinas, and their modern followers have already reached.

Annotated References

Aquinas, St. Thomas. 1947. *The Summa Theologica of St. Thomas Aquinas I*. Trans. by Fathers of the English Dominican Province. (New York: Benziger Brothers, Inc.).

---- 1955. *Summa Contra Gentiles – Book One*. Trans. by Anton C. Pegis. (New York: Doubleday & Company, Inc.).

-----1988. *On Being and Essence*. Trans. and interp by Joseph Bobik. (Notre Dame: Notre Dame University Press). Particularly Chapters Three and Four.

On the uncaused cause, see 1947 (*Summa Theologica*) I Q2 art 3.

On the uncaused cause as pure act of existing, see 1955 (*Summa Congent*) Bk 1. Ch. 16. Par. 3.

On absolute simplicity, see 1947 (*Summa Theologica*) I Q3 art 7.

On the uniqueness of the uncaused cause, see 1955 (*Summa Congent*) Bk 1. Ch. 42. Par. 3.

On the infinity of the one uncaused cause, see 1955 (*Summa Congent*) Bk 1. Ch. 43. Par 1&3

On the uncaused cause being a Creator, see 1947 (*Summa Theologica*) I Q 44 Art 1

Aristotle 1980. *Aristotle's Physics*. Trans. by Hippocrates G. Apostle. (Grinnell, IA: The Peripatetic Press). Particularly Book VIII.

----. 1984(a). *Metaphysics*. Trans. by W.D. Ross in The *Complete Works of Aristotle*, Vol. Two. Ed. by Jonathan Barnes. (Princeton, NJ: Princeton University Press). Particularly Book 12 (Lambda).

On the unmoved mover, see *Physics*, Book VIII (all).

On the uncaused cause as pure act and final cause, see *Metaphysics* (Book XII – Lambda).

Barr, Stephen 2006. *Modern Physics and Ancient Faith* (Notre Dame: Notre Dame University Press) (regarding a response to scientific critics of theism).

Dawkins, Richard 2006. *The God Delusion* (New York: Mariner Books) (critique of theism).

Lonergan, Bernard 1992 *Insight* (Toronto: University of Toronto Press). Particularly Chapter Nineteen.

Lonergan's Proof of God's Existence: If reality is completely intelligible, then an unrestricted intelligible must exist, and if an unconditioned intelligible exists, then it must be an unrestricted act of mentation (thinking), and as such, it must be only one and the ultimate cause (Creator) of all other intelligibility and reality. This coincides with the above proof in Steps (4) through (8).

Plato. 1961(a). *The Collected Dialogues of Plato*. Ed. by Edith Hamilton and Huntington Cairns. (Princeton, NJ: Princeton University Press). Particularly *Parmenides* and *The Sophist*.

Plato was the first to understand the primacy and unicity of Being in the *Parmenides* and *The Sophist*. Though Aristotle preferred a first cause (first mover) argument, it seems that Thomas Aquinas was able to combine both trains of thought (receiving the Platonic view from St. Augustine and other Neo-Platonists) in his masterpiece as a young man *On Being and Essence*. Readers wishing to see the true roots of the above eight-step proof will want to examine this text more closely.

Spitzer, Robert 2010. *New Proofs for the Existence of God: Contributions of Contemporary Physics and Philosophy* (Grand Rapids: Eerdmans). Particularly Chapter Three.

Chapter Three gives a contemporary metaphysical proof for the existence of God. The proof for the unrestrictedness, unicity, and causation of the first cause (the unconditioned condition) may be helpful to readers.

Evidence for a Transphysical Soul
from Near Death Experiences

(In both *Science, God & Creation* and
From Nothing to Cosmos – Episodes #3&4)

Outline of Chapter Seven Content and Power Points

Power Point #7.1

NEAR-DEATH EXPERIENCES

➤ "Clinical Death" – the absence of electrical activity in the
cerebral cortex (flat EEG) and in the lower brain (fixed and
dilated pupils; no gag reflex).
➤ Control groups experiencing clinical death but no NDE's.
➤ Same shut down of brain, same use of pharmaceuticals, and
same conditions of resuscitation.

Power Point #7.2
POWER POINT #7.2

**FOUR KINDS OF OBJECTIVE EVIDENCE OF SURVIVAL OF
CONSCIOUSNESS**

1. Veridical (verifiable) aspects of NDE's (all five major studies)
2. 80% of blind people see during NDE (Ring Study)
3. Vast majority of children/adults experience little death
   anxiety after NDE (Morse Study)

Power Point #7.3

Four Major Medical Studies of Near Death Experiences

Dr. Pim van Lommel et. al – The Lancet Study

van Lommel, MD, Pim; van Wees, Ruud; Meyers,
   Vincent; and Elfferich, Ingrid. 2001. Near-Death Experience in
   Survivors of Cardiac Arrest: A Prospective Study in the
   Netherlands."*The Lancet.* Vol. 358, Issue 9298, pp. 2039-
   2045.

Dr. Kenneth Ring – study of NDE's and the blind

Ring, Kenneth; Cooper, Sharon; and Tart, Charles. 1999.
   *Mindsight: Near-Death and Out-of-Body Experiences in the
   Blind.* (Palo Alto, CA: William James Center for Consciousness
   Studies at the Institute of Transpersonal Psychology).

Dr. Melvin Morse – study of NDE's and death anxiety in children

Morse, M.; Castillo, P.; Venecia, D.; et al. 1986. "Childhood
   Near-Death Experiences." *American Journal of Diseases of
   Children*, 140, pp. 1110-1113.

Morse, M.; Connor, D.; and Tyler, D. 1985. "Near-Death
   Experiences in a Pediatric Population." *American Journal of
   Diseases of Children*, 139, pp. 595-600.

Gallup study of NDE's

Gallup, George Jr. and Proctor, William. 1982. *Adventures in
   Immortality.* (New York: McGraw-Hill).

Review Questions and Answers (Chapter Seven)

65. Briefly describe the four verifiable kinds of evidence for the survival of human self-consciousness after bodily death that comes from near death experiences:

   a.   Clinically dead people see and hear experiential data which only occurred during their clinical death, and can be subsequently verified to have occurred.

   b.   80% of blind people (even those blind from birth) are able to see (for the first time or after a long period of time) only when they are clinically dead.

   c.   Children and adults who have had a near death experience have a significantly lowered measurable death anxiety by comparison with the population that has not had a near death experience (even those who were clinically dead, but did not have an NDE during clinical death).

   d.   Children report seeing a loving white light, or Jesus, or deceased relatives during their near death experience (even though they had never heard of a near death experience or phenomena that occurred during one). Some of the children see relatives or friends that were never mentioned to them previously, but are able to talk freely about them – what they look like and messages given to them to tell others, etc.

66. What is meant by "clinical death"?

Answer: A person who has no electrical activity in the brain (signifying a cessation of nervous activity needed for sensation and thought). This is measured by a flat eeg (indicating no electrical activity in the cerebral cortex), no gag reflex, and fixed and dilated pupils (indicating a lack of electrical activity in the other parts of the brain). The complete absence of electrical activity in the brain disallows the possibility of sensation and thought which gives rise to the question of how clinically dead people can see, hear, think and remember. They cannot be doing this through any known physical or bodily function, leading to the very real possibility that it is occurring through a transphysical source of consciousness and perception. This strongly suggests a component to human beings which is transphysical and transmaterial (which might be referred to as "a soul").

67. Briefly explain "veridical evidence" and why this is significant for showing that near death experiences include an element of perception and thought after clinical death.

Answer: "Veridical evidence" refers to verifiable evidence of a unique sort occurring during a near death experience which can be subsequently verified when a patient has returned to his or her body. True example -- a person who leaves his body, passes through the wall of a hospital and sees an old sneaker on the fifth floor ledge of the outside wall of the hospital (the experience of the sneaker and its position is unique – not common to the vast majority of near death experiences). A researcher crawls out on the fifth floor ledge of the hospital and finds the sneaker there (probably dropped by a construction worker) and had been there for decades (verifiable after the NDE). These findings have been corroborated by many studies. Dr. Pim van Lommel's well-known 2001 longitudinal study in multiple Dutch hospitals (reported in Great Britain's prestigious medical journal, *The Lancet*) indicated that veridical evidence was so considerable as to be undeniable (see Pim van Lommel, MD, Vincent Ruud van Wees, and Ingrid Elfferich, 2001 "Near Death Experience in Survivors of Cardiac Arrest: A Prospective Study in the Netherlands." *The Lancet.* Vol. 358, Issue 9298, pp. 2039-2045).

One researcher, Janice Holden made a compendium of 107 cases in thirty-nine studies by thirty-seven authors in 2007 in which veridical experiences had been reported. She concluded as follows:

"Using the most stringent criterion – that a case would be classified as inaccurate if even one detail was found to not correspond to reality – Holden found that only 8 percent involved some inaccuracy. In contrast, 37 percent of the cases – almost five times as many – were determined to be accurate by an independent objective source, such as the investigation of researchers reporting the cases." The other 55 percent did not involve inaccuracies, but could not be completely independently verified by other sources. It is difficult to believe that this degree of verifiably accurate reporting which occurred at a time when there was no electrical activity in the cortex can be attributed to a bodily function. This implies a transphysical component to human consciousness (termed "a soul"). For Holden's research, see Christopher Carter 2010. *Science and the Near Death Experience*. (Rochester, Inner Traditions) pp. 216-217.

68. Why do medical teams researching the experience of blind people find this particular kind of evidence so convincing for showing a transphysical dimension (capable of surviving bodily death) of human beings?

Answer: The evidence of blind people seeing after clinical death simply has no physical explanation. Without electrical activity in the brain, it does not seem possible for anyone to see; but when we can verify that sight occurs in people who were formerly blind -- many of whom were blind from birth – and so are seeing for the first time *only* when they are clinically dead, there does not seem to be *any* physical causation for it. This is why Dr. Pim van Lommel believes it to be exceedingly persuasive evidence of the survival of human consciousness after bodily death. Dr. Kenneth Ring and his team did a study of blind people and determined that 80% of blind people undergoing a near death experience could see during clinical death (and those who were blind from birth – could see for the first and only time during clinical death). When blind people return to their physical bodies, they return to a state of blindness (see Kenneth Ring, Sharon Cooper, and Charles Tart 1999, 1999. *Mindsight: Near Death and Out-of-Body Experiences in the Blind*. (Palo Alto, CA: William James Center for Consciousness Studies at the Institute of Transpersonal Psychology).

69. Explain why a "significantly lower death anxiety" (in children who experienced an NDE) is an important verification of cognitive activity after clinical death.

Answer: Dr. Melvin Morse (University of Washington Medical School) published two significant studies in the American Journal of Diseases of Children. In it he reported that children who underwent clinical death and experienced an NDE had almost no measurable death anxiety, whereas children who underwent clinical death and did not experience an NDE had a higher measurable death anxiety than even the normal population. This was true in almost every measurable case. Furthermore, the absence of death anxiety (in the children who had an NDE) continued well into adulthood, and the higher than normal death anxiety (in children who did not have an NDE) continued well into their adulthood. If death anxiety is not something that adults can control voluntarily, then there must be some other cause of the absence of death anxiety that occurs almost universally in those who did not have an NDE, and is absent from those who did have an NDE. It seems that the very real cause of the absence of death anxiety is linked to the NDE itself. But the NDE occurred when there was no electrical activity in the brain (when the physical body was clinically dead). How can there be a real causative effect produced by an apparently *non-physical* cause or source? If the cause is real, but not physical, then it seems as if it is transphysical, implying survival of human consciousness after bodily death.

See Melvin Morse, M.D., P. Castillo, and D. Venecia, 1986. "Childhood Near Death Experiences." *American Journal of Diseases of Children*, 140, pp. 1110-1113.

See Melvin Morse, M.D. D. Connor, and D. Tyler, D. 1985. "Near Death Experiences in a Pediatric Population." *American Journal of Diseases of Children*, 139, pp. 595-600.

70. Explain why certain reports of "crossing to the other side" during a near death experience has some verifiable value.

Answer: According to five major studies (von Lommel, Ring, Morse, Moody, and Gallup), it is very common for people to report seeing deceased relatives or friends when they cross over to the non-physical domain. The most interesting cases are those of children (who have no agenda) reporting that they were greeted by relatives or friends of their parents who they had never seen or heard of – mostly because they died prior to the children being born. The children could sometimes give vivid descriptions of what these relatives and friends look like when they were younger, and give personal details about the relatives' or friends' relationship with their parents. The question arises as to how they could possibly know this information after clinical death when they were seemingly unaware of it prior to clinical death. Though this evidence is circumstantial, it is so frequent that it is very difficult to ignore or simply pass over as fantasy. For this reason many researchers consider it to be circumstantially valid, though not empirically valid (like veridical evidence or the blind seeing or the lowering of death anxiety).

71. Why do many medical teams (doing extensive research on near death experiences) believe that the four phenomena mentioned above are *not* explicable by some material or physical cause (such as oxygen deprivation, narcotic or psychotropic drugs, or the shutting down of the brain)?

Answer: There are three reasons for their conclusions:

a) Only about 20% of the population undergoing clinical death has a near death experience (there are many theories about why this is so, but this will not be discussed here). If 100% of the patients were deprived of oxygen, and 100% received some kind of morphine or other narcotic for the purposes of controlling pain, and 100% experienced a shutting down of the brain (to the point of no electrical activity whatsoever), then one would expect that 100% of the patients should have a near death experience **if** near death experiences were caused by these same physical circumstances. The fact is, the circumstances are carefully measured and observed in 100% of the cases (in peer-reviewed longitudinal studies) and only 20% of the patients have had an NDE. The above argument was offered by Dr. Pim von Lommel after his careful study (with control groups) of both kinds of patients.

b) The four phenomena mentioned above all have dimensions that cannot be explained by a body undergoing the process of physical death. They have elements which cannot be explained by physical causation. For example, a person who sees a shoe on the ledge on the outside of a hospital eight stories high must have some other source of data besides merely being deprived of oxygen or taking morphine, etc. The accuracy, situational nature, and unusual characteristics of the data require some form of perceptual activity beyond a morphine induced state, or an oxygen induced state. There must be a cause sufficient to properly explain the unusual situational data, and generic physical causes (such as morphine) do not meet this requirement. This inadequacy of causal explanation also applies to blind people seeing accurately for the first time; it also applies to the problem of children reporting data about, say, dead relatives, about whom they had never heard.

c)   In virtually every case of a child having a near death experience, the death anxiety was measurably lowered; however, this does not occur in all children who experienced clinical death. In the 80% of children who experienced clinical death, but not a near death experience, the death anxiety was actually higher than the normal population. If the lowering of the death anxiety were attributable to generic physical causes, it would seem that 100% of those experiencing clinical death would also experience the lower death anxiety. Instead, this only occurs in the 20% who had the NDE (it is a very statistically sharp distinction).

72. Is there any evidence for God which comes from near death experiences? Explain.

Answer. Normally, near death experiences are used to give empirical and circumstantial evidence of the survival of human self-consciousness after bodily death (the existence of a soul). But there is also circumstantial evidence from the five major studies (von Lommel, Ring, Morse, Moody, and Gallup) for the existence of a transcendent being and a transcendent domain ("the other side"). A statistically significant percentage of those having an NDE, also see a loving white light they identify as God, or frequently in the case of children, a being who identifies himself as Jesus. Also, as in the case of Dr. Eben Alexander, there is a clear awareness of a blissful transcendent domain (which is frequently associated with "heaven"). Though this evidence is only circumstantial (and not empirical like veridical evidence), it is reported so frequently that it may have statistically significant circumstantial validity.

Four Kinds of Evidence for Transcendence
(God & Human Soul)

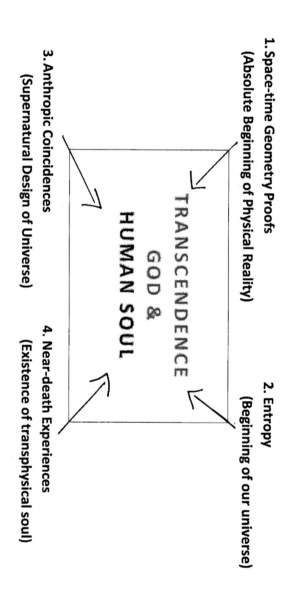

1. Space-time Geometry Proofs
(Absolute Beginning of Physical Reality)

2. Entropy
(Beginning of our universe)

TRANSCENDENCE
GOD &
HUMAN SOUL

3. Anthropic Coincidences
(Supernatural Design of Universe)

4. Near-death Experiences
(Existence of transphysical soul)

Quotations and References of Major Scientists and Physicians

I.   Quotations

A.   Dr. Pim van Lommel's general conclusion to his longitudinal study (in *The Lancet*).

How could a clear consciousness outside one's body be experienced at the moment that the brain no longer functions during a period of clinical death with flat EEG? . . . Furthermore, blind people have described veridical perception during out-of-body experiences at the time of this experience. NDE pushes at the limits of medical ideas about the range of human consciousness and the mind-brain relation. In our prospective study of patients that were clinically dead (flat EEG, showing no electrical activity in the cortex and loss of brain stem function evidenced by fixed dilated pupils and absence of the gag reflex) the patients report a clear consciousness, in which cognitive functioning, emotion, sense of identity, or memory from early childhood occurred, as well as perceptions from a position out and above their 'dead' body.[42]

B.   Dr. Eben Alexander's assessment of his measured physiological condition during the time of his near death experience.

"My synapses—the spaces between the neurons of the brain that support the electrochemical activity that makes the brain function—were not simply compromised during my experience. They were stopped. Only isolated pockets of deep cortical neurons were still sputtering, but no broad networks capable of generating anything like what we call 'consciousness.' The E. coli bacteria that flooded my brain during my illness made sure of that. My doctors have told me that according to all the brain tests they were doing, there was no way that any of the functions including vision, hearing, emotion, memory, language, or logic could possibly have been intact.[43]

---

[42] van Lommel, et al 2001.
[43] Alexander 2012 (b) p 10

C. Dr. Kenneth Ring's conclusion to his study of blind patients.

Among those narrating NDEs, not only did their experiences conform to the classic NDE pattern, but they did not even vary according to the specific sight status of our respondents; that is, whether an NDEr was born blind or had lost his or her sight in later life, or even (as in a few of our cases) had some minimal light perception only, the NDEs described were much the same.

Furthermore, 80 percent of our thirty-one blind respondents claimed to be able to see during their NDEs or OBEs, and, like Vicki and Brad, often told us that they could see objects and persons in the physical world, as well as features of otherworldly settings.[44] ... Ring et al also found that the quality of perception was quite high among the majority of blind patients who reported seeing during their near-death experience:

How well do our respondents find they can see during these episodes? We have, of course, already noted that the visual perceptions of Vicki and Brad were extremely clear and detailed, especially when they found themselves in the otherworldly portion of their near-death journey. While not all of our blind NDErs had clear, articulated visual impressions, nevertheless enough of them did, so that we can conclude that cases like Vicki's and Brad's are quite representative in this regard.[45]

D. Janice Holden's General Conclusion Regarding the Accuracy of Reported Data During Clinical Death.

Janice Holden made a compendium of 107 cases in thirty-nine studies by thirty-seven authors in 2007[46] in which veridical (verifiable) experiences had been reported. She concluded as follows:

---

[44] Ring and Valarino 2006, p. 81.
[45] Ring and Valarino 2006, p. 81.
[46] Holden 2007, pp. 33-42.

Using the most stringent criterion – that a case would be classified as inaccurate if even one detail was found to not correspond to reality – Holden found that only 8 percent involved some inaccuracy. In contrast, 37 percent of the cases – almost five times as many – were determined to be accurate by an independent objective source, such as the investigation of research reporting the cases.[47]

The other 55 percent did not involve inaccuracies, but could not be completely independently verified by other sources.

E. Dr. Melvin Morse's general conclusion regarding lower death anxiety in children having an NDE:

We discovered that adults who have had near-death experiences as children have a much lower fear of death than people who have not had them. This was true whether they had vivid and wonderful memories of a flower-filled heaven or a brief and fleeting experience of light. Furthermore, the deeper their experience, the less they were afraid of death. This finding is in sharp contrast to people who have come close to death and survived, but were not fortunate enough to have had a near-death experience. They actually had a slightly higher death anxiety than normal. And…people who identify themselves as being intensely spiritual, have the same death anxiety as the general population.[48]

F. Summary of the Gallup Survey Data:

George Gallup Jr. in a 1982 Gallup Poll discovered that approximately 8 million adults in the United States had had a near-death experience (a significantly large population from which to take accurate samples). The people sampled reported having some of the following ten characteristics, which appear to be unique to near-death experiences:[49]

---

[47] Carter, 2010, p. 217.
[48] Morse 1992, p. 66.
[49] See Gallup and Proctor 1982.

Out of body	26%
Accurate visual perception	23%
Audible sounds or voices	17%
Feelings of peace, painlessness	32%
Light phenomena	14%
Life review	32%
Being in another world	32%
Encountering other beings	23%
Tunnel experience	9%
Precognition	6%

G. Sir Arthur Eddington (Physicist) Assessed the Need for a Transphysical "Human Spirit" to Perform Uniquely Human Creative Functions:

We all know that there are regions of the human spirit untrammeled by the world of physics. In the mystic sense of the creation around us, in the expression of art, in a yearning towards God, the soul grows upward and finds the fulfillment of something implanted in its nature. The sanction for this development is within us, a striving born with our consciousness or an Inner Light proceeding from a greater power than ours. Science can scarcely question this sanction, for the pursuit of science springs from a striving which the mind is impelled to follow, a questioning that will not be suppressed. Whether in the intellectual pursuits of science or in the mystical pursuits of the spirit, the light beckons ahead and the purpose surging in our nature responds.[50]

---

[50] Eddington 1928, pp. 327-28.

II. References

Alexander, Eben, M.D. 2012 (a). *Proof of Heaven: A Neurosurgeon's Journey into the Afterlife* (New York: Simon and Schuster). -2012 (b) "The Science of Heaven" *Newsweek* (November 18, 2012).

Carter, Christopher. 2010. *Science and the Near-Death Experience.* (Rochester, Inner Traditions).

Eddington, Sir Arthur. 1928. *The Nature of the Physical World.* (Cambridge: Cambridge University Press).

Gallup, George Jr. and Proctor, William. 1982. *Adventures in Immortality.* (New York: McGraw-Hill).

Holden, Janice. 2007. "More things in Heaven and Earth: A Response to Near-Death Experiences with Hallucinatory Features" in *Journal of Near-Death Studies* 26, no.1 (Fall 2007): 33-42.

Moody, Raymond A. 1975. *Life After Life.* (New York: Harper Collins).

----.1988. *The Light Beyond.* (New York: Bantam Books).

----.1993. *Reunions: Visionary Encounters with Departed Loved Ones.* (New York: Random House).

Morse, MD, Melvin. 1990. *Closer to the Light: Learning from the Near-Death Experiences of Children.* (New York: Random House).

----. 1992. *Transformed by the Light.* (New York: Ballantine Books).

Morse, M.; Castillo, P.; Venecia, D.; et al. 1986. "Childhood Near-Death Experiences." *American Journal of Diseases of Children*, 140, pp. 1110-1113.

Morse, M.; Connor, D.; and Tyler, D. 1985. "Near-Death Experiences in a Pediatric Population." *American Journal of Diseases of Children*, 139, pp. 595-600.

Ring, PhD. Kenneth. 1980. *Life at Death: A Scientific Investigation of the Near-Death Experience.* (New York: Coward, McCann & Geoghegan).

Ring, Kenneth; Cooper, Sharon; and Tart, Charles. 1999. *Mindsight: Near-Death and Out-of-Body Experiences in the Blind.* (Palo Alto, CA: William James Center for Consciousness Studies at the Institute of Transpersonal Psychology).

Ring, Kenneth, and Valarino, Evelyn Elsaesser. 2006. *Lessons from the Light: What we can learn from the near-death experience.* (New York: Insight Books).

van Lommel, MD, Pim; van Wees, Ruud; Meyers, Vincent; and Elfferich, Ingrid. 2001. "Near-Death Experience in Survivors of Cardiac Arrest: A Prospective Study in the Netherlands." *The Lancet.* Vol. 358, Issue 9298, pp. 2039-2045.

Brief Biographies of Key Scientists/Physicians

Dr. Eben Alexander: Eben Alexander III is an American neurosurgeon. He attended the Duke University School of Medicine (M.D., 1980). Alexander has taught at Duke University Medical Center, Brigham and Women's Hospital, Harvard Medical School, University of Massachusetts Medical School, and the University of Virginia Medical School. He is the author of the best-selling *Proof of Heaven: A Neurosurgeon's Journey into the Afterlife*, in which he describes his 2008 near death experience and asserts that science can and will determine that heaven really does exist.

Dr. Raymond Moody: Raymond A. Moody, Jr. is a psychologist and medical doctor. He is most famous as an author of books about life after death and near-death experiences. He earned a Ph.D. in philosophy and a Ph.D. in psychology as well as an M.D. Moody is Chair of Consciousness Studies at the University of Nevada, Las Vegas.

[51]He was forerunner of the movement to do controlled medical studies of near death experience, and has published widely on the results of those studies.

---

[51] Wikipedia 2013 "Raymond Moody" http://en.wikipedia.org/wiki/Raymond_Moody

Dr. Melvin Morse: Melvin Morse earned his medical degree in 1980. After completing his medical degree he specialized in pediatrics and neuro-oncology. From 1985 to 2007 Morse served on the medical faculty at the University of Washington. He is the author of several books on the near death experience, in which he offers conclusions based on interviewing children who came close to dying.[52] He has published his findings in the American Journal of Diseases of Children (The Journal of the American Medical Association).

Dr. Kenneth Ring: Kenneth Ring is Professor Emeritus of psychology at the University of Connecticut, and a researcher within the field of near-death studies. Ring is the co-founder and past president of the International Association for Near-Death Studies and is the founding editor of the *Journal of Near-Death Studies*.[53] He has made an extensive study of sight in blind patients during death experiences.

Dr. Pim van Lommel: Pim van Lommel is a Dutch cardiologist and scientist. Van Lommel studied medicine at Utrecht University, specializing in cardiology. He worked as a cardiologist at the Rijnstate Hospital, Arnhem, for 26 years (1977-2003). Van Lommel is best known for his scientific work on the subjects of near-death experiences and consciousness, including a prospective study published in the medical journal The Lancet. He is also the author of the 2007 Dutch book] titled *Endless Consciousness: A scientific approach to the near-death experience (Eindeloos Bewustzijn: een wetenschappelijke visie op de Bijna-Dood Ervaring),* which has been translated to German, English, French, and Spanish.[54]

[52] Wikipedia 2013 ""Melvin Morse" http://en.wikipedia.org/wiki/Melvin_L._Morse
[53] Wikipedia 2013 "Kenneth Ring" http://en.wikipedia.org/wiki/Kenneth_Ring
[54] Wikipedia 2013 "Pim van Lommel" http://en.wikipedia.org/wiki/Pim_van_Lommel

Evidence of a Transphysical Soul from the Five Transcendental Desires

(In only *From Nothing to Cosmos* – Episode #4)

Outline of Chapter Eight Content and Power Points

Power Point #8.1

Four Step Argument from Transcendental Desire to a Soul

1. We have five desires for the perfect and unconditional - - the desire for perfect and unconditional truth, love, justice/goodness, beauty and being.
2. We must have an awareness of what we desire; therefore we must have an awareness of perfect truth, love, justice/goodness, beauty and being.
3. We have the capacity to recognize every imperfection in our experience of truth love, justice/goodness, beauty and being which would not be possible unless we were aware of *perfection* in them.
4. The source of our awareness of perfect truth, love, justice/goodness, beauty and being must be perfect truth, love, justice/goodness, beauty and being themselves; so we must be connected with that Transcendental Source.

CONCLUSION

Power Point #8.2
Truth

How can you recognize every time you have not arrived at an answer concerning "everything about everything" unless you had some awareness of what "everything about everything" would be like?

The source of our tacit awareness of what "everything about everything" would be like must be the idea of "everything about everything" (a perfect act of thinking).

The Unity of the Five Transcendentals

Perfect truth, perfect love, perfect justice/goodness, perfect beauty and perfect being must all be absolutely simple but there can be only one absolutely simple reality – the pure, unrestricted act of existing through itself (see above Chapter Six for proof).

Therefore, truth, perfect love, perfect justice/goodness, perfect beauty and perfect being must be one in the same reality - - **God**

Truth

If we have access to an act of perfect thinking (the idea of everything about everything) and the act of perfect thinking is God, then God must be present to us as the creative horizon of our thinking - - We are transcendent.

Power Point #8.3
Love

1. We recognize every imperfection in others' and our acts of love.
2. How are we able to recognize every imperfection in love if we do not have some tacit awareness of what perfect love would be like?
3. The source of our tacit awareness of what perfect love would be like must be perfect love itself, and if perfect love itself is God, then God is present to us as the transcendent horizon of perfect love.
   Therefore you are transcendent.

Justice and Fairness

1. We also have the capacity to recognize every imperfect manifestation of justice and fairness in the conduct of others, ourselves, in the law, and in society.
2. How can we be aware of every manifestation of imperfect justice or fairness unless we have some tacit awareness of perfect justice or fairness to compare it to?
3. The source of our tacit awareness of perfect justice and fairness must be perfect justice and fairness itself, and if this is God, then God is present to us as the horizon of perfect justice and fairness.

Beauty

1. We recognize every imperfection in beauty in ourselves, others, and nature.
2. How can we recognize every imperfection in beauty unless we have some tacit awareness of perfect beauty to compare it to?
3. The source of our tacit awareness of perfect beauty must be perfect beauty itself, and if this is God, then God is present to us as the horizon of perfect beauty.

Study Questions for Chapter Eight

73. What are the indications that human beings have an awareness of and desire for perfect and unconditional truth?

Answer:

a. *We have a desire to know everything about everything.* Human beings want to know everything about everything. Another way of saying this is to say they desire to know the complete set of correct answers to the complete set of questions. Some philosophers call this the desire for complete intelligibility (Lonergan).

b. *We must have awareness of what we desire.* Now, you cannot desire what you are not aware of. In other words, some kind of awareness is necessary to incite both desire and anticipation of the desire's fulfillment. People can obtain awareness sufficient to engender desire *from experience of the sensible world.* The awareness of "everything about everything" sufficient to engender the desire for it is quite different. *One cannot experience "everything about everything" in order to engender the desire for it.* We seem to have an awareness of what is in principle always beyond our experience or any achievement of our acts of understanding!

c. *Evidence of our tacit awareness of what complete intelligibility would be like.* Is there any evidence for our having this awareness of "everything about everything" besides needing an awareness sufficient to engender our desire for it? Yes. It seems that human beings have an unrestricted desire to know. No matter how far we have come in gaining knowledge, we will continue to ask questions every time we realize that we have not yet arrived at a knowledge of "everything about everything." The interesting thing is that we always seem to know that we have not yet arrived at this final point, and this *awareness* of incomplete or imperfect knowledge informs us that we have reached a limit. When you think about it, you really cannot know you have reached a limit unless you have a sense that there is something beyond it. For example, if you did not know that there was something beyond a wall, all you would see is opaqueness blocking your vision – you wouldn't call it "a wall" or "a boundary" or a "limit." If human beings really do have the capacity to ask subsequent questions indefinitely until they get to "everything about everything," you might wonder what is this awareness "beyond every single answer that we get to," which informs us that we have reached a limit that we can go beyond, engendering indefinite questions until we reach the knowledge of "everything about everything." Let's call this "a tacit awareness of what complete intelligibility would be like." Whenever we get an answer to a question, we seem to compare it to this horizon of what complete intelligibility would be like, which makes us immediately aware that our previous answer was incomplete. The moment we are aware of the incomplete intelligibility of the previous answer, we ask a subsequent question (with a sense of where we must turn to get to the answer). We will seemingly do this indefinitely until we get to the complete set of answers to the complete set of questions. This is what makes human intelligence creative making it quite distinct from artificial intelligence which does nothing like this (perhaps because artificial intelligence has no horizon of the completeness of intelligibility, and we have no way of giving this to a machine).

d. *The notional awareness of what complete intelligibility would be like.* Notice that our awareness of the completeness of intelligibility is notional or tacit. It is clearly not an explicit awareness of "everything about everything," because we don't know everything about everything – we have literally millions of questions that remain unanswered. So, what kind of awareness is it? Bernard Lonergan calls it "notional awareness" – what might be termed a tacit (non-discursive) awareness of a complete whole. This dovetails with what we term "a horizon of what complete intelligibility would be like." Though we are tacitly aware of what complete intelligibility would be like, we do not have an explicit knowledge of complete intelligibility. This tacit awareness of what complete intelligibility would be like is sufficient to inform us of the incompleteness of any answer at which we might have arrived (that is not completely intelligible). This tacit awareness of what complete intelligibility would be like acts as a kind of desirable goal as well as a point of comparison for any particular answer at which we might have arrived.

e. *The tacit awareness of what complete intelligibility would be like is innate.* How can we have a tacit or notional awareness of the completeness of intelligibility? Could we have gotten this from our experience? Clearly not, because all of our experiences are radically incomplete (restricted by space, time, magnitude, modalities, etc.). Could we have gotten it from our aggregated knowledge? Clearly not, because in as much as our aggregated knowledge gives rise to subsequent questions, it too must be incomplete, disallowing it from being the basis of our tacit awareness of what complete intelligibility would be like. So where did we get this from? It seems as if it is a basic constituent of our intelligence prior to any experience or act of understanding – tantamount to an innate notion (as distinct from an innate idea which has specific contents).

f.   *God is the source of the innate notional (tacit) awareness of what complete intelligibility would be like.* What could be the source of this innate notion of what complete intelligibility would be like? It seems that it would have to be complete intelligibility itself. Everything short of complete intelligibility is incomplete, and therefore would be incapable of conveying what complete intelligibility would be like. Well, what is complete intelligibility itself? It is a perfect act of mentation or thinking – a perfect unity of all intelligibility – which would seem to be absolutely simple (see above Chapter Six, Steps (7) and (8)) – which would have to be the one (and only one) unconditioned, unrestricted Creator (termed "God").

g.   *God is present to human consciousness making it transcendent.* What does it mean to say that we are notionally aware of the perfectly mentative dimension of God (the one unconditioned unrestricted Creator)? It would seem that God would have to reveal to us innately and notionally what complete intelligibility would be like (which he is -- in his perfect act of mentation or thinking – see Chapter Six, Step (7)). This innate notional awareness of what complete intelligibility would be like (which has its origin in God) is what causes all human questioning, creativity, and striving for the complete set of answers to the complete set of questions. For this reason it seems that human beings are transcendent – they are capable of being aware of God's mentative presence, and God is present to this awareness. This sheds light on the scripture that human beings are made in the image and likeness of God (Genesis 1:26).

74. What are the indications that human beings have a desire for perfect and unconditional love?

Answer: Human beings appear to have a tacit awareness of *perfect and unconditional Love.* Not only do we have the power to love (i.e., the power to be naturally connected to another human being in profound emotion, care, self-gift, concern, and acceptance), we have a tacit awareness of what this profound interpersonal connection would be like if it were perfect. This tacit awareness of perfect Love has the positive effect of inciting us to pursue ever more perfect forms of love. However, it has the drawback of inciting us to *expect* ever more perfect love from other human beings. This generally leads to frustrated expectations of others and consequently to a decline of relationships that can never grow fast enough to match this expectation of perfect and unconditional love.

75. Why do some philosophers think that this desire for perfect and unconditional love indicates human transcendentality (and even the presence of the divine within us)?

Answer: The origin of our desire for unconditional love is similar to the origin of our desire for perfect truth (complete intelligibility). Just as our unrestricted desire to know must include a *notional* awareness of what complete intelligibility would be like (to give rise to an awareness of and dissatisfaction with every manifestation of incomplete intelligibility), so also the desire for unconditional love must include a notional awareness of unconditional love to give rise to the awareness of and dissatisfaction with every manifestation of conditioned and imperfect love. This notional awareness of what unconditional love would be like seems to be beyond any specifically known or concretely experienced love, for it seems to cause dissatisfaction with every conditioned love we have known or experienced. Thus, our dissatisfaction would seem to arise out of an ideal of perfect or unconditional love which has neither been experienced nor actualized. How can we have an awareness of perfect or unconditional love that we have neither known nor experienced? How can we even extrapolate to it if we do not know where we are going? The inability to give a logical answer to these questions has led some philosophers to associate the desire for perfect or unconditional love with "the notion of unconditional love within us," which would seem to have its source in unconditional love itself.

76. What are the indications that human beings have a desire for perfect and unconditional goodness/ justice?

Answer: As with the notional awareness of perfect and unconditional truth and love, philosophers have long recognized the human desire for *perfect justice or goodness.* Not only do human beings have a sense of good and evil, a capacity for moral reflection, a profoundly negative felt awareness of cooperation with evil (guilt), and a profoundly positive felt awareness of cooperation with goodness (nobility), they also have a "sense" of what perfect justice/ goodness would be like. Human beings are not content to simply act in accordance with their conscience in the here and now, they are constantly striving for ways to achieve the more noble, the greater good, the higher ideal. They even go so far as to pursue the perfectly good or just order.

Evidently there is a host of well-meaning, dedicated, and generous men and women who have tried to extract perfect and unconditional justice from the legal system and the ideals of social justice from institutions dedicated to the common good. The despairing rhetoric of dashed idealism and cynicism does not belong solely to early Marxism; it can be found in public defenders who decry the legal system for prosecuting the innocent, and victims who vilify the very same system for letting the guilty go free. It can also be found in educators who criticize the educational system for not setting high enough standards, and in community advocates who tear down the very same system for making the standards too high and too exclusive. But our imperfect world will not allow either side to be *perfectly* correct. Many philosophers believe that these frustrations and dashed expectations have a common source – the desire for perfect justice and goodness.

77. Why do some philosophers think that this desire for perfect and unconditional justice/goodness indicates human transcendentality (and even the presence of the divine within us)?

Answer: What is the source of our notional awareness of

perfect justice/goodness? As with the desire for complete intelligibility and unconditional love, the desire for perfect justice/goodness seems to go beyond any experience or knowledge of justice we could possibly have. Our frustrated idealism reveals that we continually see the limits of any current manifestation of justice and goodness which, in turn, reveals that we are already beyond those limits. Given that our desire for justice/goodness will only be satisfied when we reach perfect, unconditional justice/goodness, it would seem that our desire is guided by a notional awareness of perfect, unconditional justice/goodness, and given that such a notion of perfect, unconditional justice/goodness cannot be obtained from a conditioned and imperfect world, it would seem that its source is from perfect, unconditional justice/goodness itself. For this reason, philosophers have associated this notion of perfect, unconditional justice/goodness with the presence of God to human consciousness.

78. What are the indications that human beings have a desire for perfect and unconditional beauty?

Answer: The desire for perfect and unconditional beauty is most easily seen in our dissatisfactions with beauty in our everyday life. We don't look good enough and neither do other people. The house is not perfect enough, the painting can never achieve perfection, and the musical composition, though beautiful beyond belief, could always be better. Once in a great while, we think we have arrived at consummate beauty. This might occur while looking at a scene of natural beauty: a sunset over the water, majestic green and brown mountains against a horizon of blue sky; but even there, despite our desire to elevate it to the quasi-divine, we get bored and strive for a different or an even more perfect manifestation of natural beauty – a *little* better sunset, another vantage point of the Alps that's a *little* more perfect.

We will always grow bored or frustrated with any imperfect manifestation of beauty. This causes us to try to make perfectly beautiful what is imperfect by nature. It is true that a garden can achieve a certain perfection of beauty, but our continuous desire to improve it can make us grow terribly dissatisfied when we cannot perfect it indefinitely. It is this desire to "make the beautiful more perfect indefinitely" that leads some philosophers to conclude that we have a desire for perfect and unconditional beauty.

79. Why do some philosophers think that this desire for perfect and unconditional beauty indicates human transcendentality (and even the presence of the divine within us)?

Answer: Recall that dissatisfaction with even the most beautiful objects of our experience reveals our ability to indefinitely perceive the limits of *imperfect* beauty, which, in turn, reveals our ability to be beyond those limits, which, in turn, reveals a notional awareness of what perfect beauty would be like (a notional awareness of a beauty without imperfection or limit). Since it seems that the notion of perfect beauty cannot be obtained or abstracted from a world of sensorial (imperfect) beauty, or even from the beauty of great ideals, goods, and truths (because they too are conditioned and imperfect), one is led to the conjecture that its source arises out of perfect beauty itself. For this reason, some philosophers have associated the notion of perfect beauty with the notional presence of perfect beauty (i.e., God) to human consciousness.

Annotated References

Aquinas, St. Thomas. 1947. *The Summa Theologica of St. Thomas Aquinas* I. Trans. by Fathers of the English Dominican Province. (New York: Benziger Brothers, Inc.).

---- 1955. *Summa Contra Gentiles – Book One*. Trans. by Anton C. Pegis. (New York: Doubleday & Company, Inc.).

On absolute simplicity as perfect perfection and as only one being, see 1955 (*Summa ConGent*) Bk 1 Ch. 42, par. 3.

Balthasar, Hans Urs von. 1982. *The Glory of the Lord: A Theological Aesthetics*. Trans. by Erasmo Leiva-Merikakis. (Edinburgh: T&T Clark) (regarding the desire for the beautiful).

Lonergan, Bernard. 1972. *Method in Theology*. (New York: Herder and Herder) (regarding perfect truth and perfect goodness and perfect love).

----. 1992. *Insight: A Study of Human Understanding*. In *Collected Works of Bernard Lonergan 3*, ed. by Frederick E. Crowe and Robert M. Doran. (Toronto: University of Toronto Press) (regarding perfect truth and perfect goodness).

Newman, John Henry. 1961. Unpublished manuscript entitled "Proof of Theism." Ed. by Adrian Boekraad and Henry Tristram in *The Argument from Conscience to the Existence of God*. (London: Mill Hill) (regarding the desire for perfect justice and goodness).

Plato. 1961(b). *The Republic* Trans. by Paul Shorey. In *The Collected Dialogues of Plato*. Ed. by Edith Hamilton and Huntington Cairns. (Princeton, NJ: Princeton University Press) (regarding the desire for perfect justice and goodness).

----. 1993. *Symposium and Phaedrus*. Trans. by Benjamin Jowett. (New York: Dover Publications) (regarding the desire for perfect beauty and also for perfect love, truth, and goodness).

Spitzer, Robert 2010. (Grand Rapids: Eerdmans). *New Proofs for the Existence of God: Contributions of Contemporary Physics and Philosophy.* (Grand Rapids: Eerdmans) Particularly Chapters Seven and Eight (regarding the desire for perfect love, truth, goodness, beauty, and home).

Stein, Edith. 1989. *On the Problem of Empathy*. Trans. By Waltraut Stein. (Washington, D.C.: Institute of Carmelite Studies Publications) (regarding the desire for perfect-love/empathy).

Atheism, the Bible & Science, Evolution, and Aliens

(In only *From Nothing to Cosmos* – Episode #4)

Outline of Chapter Nine Content and Power Points

Power Point #9.1
Atheism vs. The Evidence

Atheism is not rational - - it is a personal choice.
Four major reasons for intellectual atheism:

(1)   Inability to reconcile suffering with a loving God
(2)   Belief that religion has done more harm than good.
(3)   Persistent naturalism.
(4)   The refusal to be responsible to a moral authority outside of oneself.

The Bible and Science

The bible and science are not irreconcilable because they are doing two different things.

- The Bible gives revealed truths of salvation
- Natural science uses empirical-mathematical method to come to a description of the physical universe.

God reveals truths of salvation through categories that the biblical author and his audience can understand.

- Scientific accuracy is not essential to revealing truths of salvation. Indeed, it can run contrary to this, because the categories and methods of scientific explanation would have been completely beyond the audience to whom God was revealing himself (Israel in 600 to 500 B.C.).
- What was God's intention in revealing himself to the biblical author? To correct four major errors in the creation myths of the day (e.g. the Gilgamesh Epic).
  (i)   One God versus many gods.
  (ii)   God creates all natural objects versus divinity ascribed to natural objects (e.g. the sun god).
  (iii) Human beings are made in the image and likeness of God versus human beings are "play things" for the gods' capricious activities.
  (iv)   The material world is essentially good versus the material world is frequently evil.

Power Point #9.2
The Bible and Evolution

Catholics may believe in evolution (as scientifically verified) so long as they do not deny the existence of a transphysical soul (Pope Pius XII).

- Pope Pius XII Encyclical letter *Humani Generis* (1950).

Aliens
- There are 10^{22} stars in 10^{11} galaxies in our universe. Many of these stars have planets which might accommodate a life form.
- Catholics can remain open to the possibility of other life forms in our universe.
- If aliens are intelligent life forms (similar to human beings with creativity and an awareness of the five transcendental desires) we would have to assume that they had a "soul" (capable of surviving bodily death). Since a soul is transphysical, God would have to create the souls of aliens outside of a physical process.
- If intelligent aliens are encountered, then catechize and baptize them.
- Christ's redemptive act is sufficient for the entire universe. It does not have to be repeated on every planet any more than it would have to be repeated in every country in the world (Israel was sufficient).

Study Questions for Chapter Nine

80. If there is so much evidence for God and a soul from contemporary science, why are there scientists who are atheists?

Scientific atheism is not scientific. As noted in Chapter One, science cannot disprove God nor can it show that the universe does not need a Creator. Conversely, as we saw in Chapters Two and Three, science (particularly contemporary physics) gives probative evidence for a beginning of any universe or multiverse (from space-time geometry proofs and entropy), as well as evidence for fine-tuning of universal constants and fine-tuning of entropy at the Big Bang which may prove to be probative if no multiverse hypothesis can be found that does not require fine-tuning of the multiverse. We also saw that careful medical studies give sound veridical evidence of the survival of human consciousness after bodily death. From this we must conclude that atheism cannot be grounded in scientific method, and that scientific method actually shows the reverse – the probability of and the reasonableness of an intelligent Creator (even of a multiverse).

So why do some scientists profess atheism? Because atheism is neither scientific nor rational – it is a personal choice that rises out of one's life circumstances and desires. Four of these choices are frequently seen among rational and scientific people:

(i)   The inability to find a rational and loving explanation for personal suffering. The question of why an all-powerful, all-loving God would allow suffering has beleaguered many because they believe that love is incompatible with suffering. However, suffering can lead to greater love by calling us out of our superficiality and making possible acts of courage, virtue, and compassion which are self-definitional. This is explained in great detail in the second Magis program called *Happiness, Suffering, & the Love of God* (see www.magisreasonfaith.org).

(ii) The belief that the world would be better off without religion (religion has done more harm than good). Many people believe that religion is a counter-force in history and culture, but this position does not reflect the reality that religion stands at the core of all culture and civilization (all over the world). Religion has given rise to virtually every legal system and societal structure; it is responsible for progress in justice (contra slavery, the development of human rights, and economic rights). It has been responsible for the advent of public hospitals and free health care, secondary and collegiate education on a large scale, the building of orphanages, etc. Without religion, the state of culture would not have progressed much beyond the stoic ethics of the Roman Empire or other similar empires in the East.

(iii) Persistent naturalism. Persistent naturalism cannot ground atheism, because naturalism cannot disprove God or a Creator. It is responsible for agnosticism because it sets a bar for belief in God that is so high that it is almost impossible to overcome. It is not unusual to hear scientists say, "I will never appeal to a supernatural cause so long as there is even the remote possibility of a natural explanation – no matter how improbable that natural cause might be." In view of this, a supernatural explanation will be ruled out a priori, but this position is not grounded in reason – it is a personal preference.

(iv) A refusal to be responsible to a moral authority outside of oneself (the desire to be a moral authority unto oneself). Quite clearly some individuals have made the choice to be responsible only to oneself, which entails not being responsible to any kind of an authority outside of oneself. Once again, this is not a decision based on objective or scientific evidence but rather a personal preference.

81. Is there a contradiction between the scientific and biblical accounts of creation?

No, because the biblical creation accounts were never intended to be scientific, instead, they are theological. The biblical author of Genesis (who lived before 500 B.C) could never have understood science as we know it. God would not have inspired the biblical author with an explanation of creation containing complex math and science which would have been completely unintelligible to him and his audience.

For Catholics, this point was clarified by Pope Pius XII in his groundbreaking Encyclical Letter *Divino Afflante Spiritu* (1943) in which he indicated that God's intention in inspiriting the biblical author was to convey *sacred truths* (truths essential for *salvation*). The objective of science is not to give sacred truths, but rather an empirical-mathematical description of the *physical* universe. It is not God's intention to convey an empirical-mathematical description of the physical universe through the bible, but rather to reveal Himself, His relationship to us, and the kind of life commensurate with His will.

82. What was God doing when he inspired the biblical author?

God was giving the biblical author theological solutions to his theological problems in the understanding of his time and day. For example, myths like the Epic of Gilgamesh (which competed with Jewish theology), portrayed the following:
a.   There were many gods,
b.   Natural objects, such as the sun, moon, stars and sea were gods, and
c.   These gods were often unjust, and fashioned the world in a way that was filled with both good and evil,

So, the biblical author had to correct these theological errors before they became confusing to the Jewish people. They needed their own creation epic to counter the errors in the rival epics, and so the biblical author was inspired to write an epic where:

a. There was one God,
b. This God created everything else such as the sun, the moon, the stars, and the seas,
c. This God was not capricious or unjust, and he certainly did not toy around with human beings,
d. He created a world which was fundamentally good (which he recognized to be "good"), and
e. He made human beings in His own image – having a divine dignity.

To read the Bible looking for a scientific explanation of creation is a misunderstanding of what divine inspiration is and how it works. Divine inspiration is not a "dictation of scientific truth," but rather an inspiration of theological truths the author and his audience could understand.

83. Why was there a need to inspire biblical authors with theological truths?

As we saw from Episodes (1) through (3), there is abundant evidence from physics and philosophy that a Creator exists who is highly intelligent. However, science and philosophy can give only limited evidence about God. So what *can* science and philosophy show or prove?

a. There is a transcendent Creator,
b. This transcendent Creator has enough power to create the universe as a whole,
c. God is one, and is not subject to space, time, or other limiting conditions, and
d. God is highly intelligent and even unrestricted in intelligence.

So what questions *can't* physics and philosophy adequately answer? Some of the very basic ones are:

a. Is God love?
b. Is God unconditional love?
c. Does God redeem suffering?
d. Does God answer prayers?
e. Does God guide us in our everyday lives?

f.   Does God make good come out of evil?

Philosophy and science can give us knowledge about the nature of a highly intelligent supernatural power, but they cannot be certain about what the super-intelligence's "heart" (emotions or feelings) is like.   There are some philosophers and scientists who believe that God is purely rational (and have no emotions or feelings to speak of). This view was held by Aristotle in the Classical Period, by many deists in the 17th through 20th centuries (including several founding fathers of the U.S.), and by many modern scientists (including Einstein).

84. What is evolution?

Evolution is a scientific theory that explains the development of species using evidence from:
a.   Fossils,
b.   Genetic similarities between species, and
c.   Geographic distribution of species.

While it may not contain a complete explanation of the development of different species, among most scientists it is the accepted naturalistic explanation for the development of higher order species.

85. Does the Bible conflict with Evolution?

Only if *naturalistic* evolution (which does not allow human beings to have a soul capable of surviving bodily death) is believed to be a complete explanation of the origin and development of all the species on earth, including humans.

Evolutionary theory seems to be in conflict with the biblical account of creation where God makes man as a separate entity in His own image apart from the animals. *Can the two accounts be reconciled?* Yes. As we saw above, the Bible is not doing science, but rather theology, and the theological point in the Genesis account is that human beings are distinct from other animals and are made in the image of God. Thus, the Catholic Church has indicated that evolutionary theory is not necessarily in conflict with its theology. This important point was clarified by Pope Pius XII in his Encyclical Letter *Humani Generis* (1950).

Catholics may believe—or not believe—in evolution to whatever degree they wish (based on the best scientific information available, of course) up to and including the development of a physical organic brain, so long as they do not exclude the existence of a soul in human beings, or claim that the soul is just a product of evolution.

This means that evolution cannot be a complete explanation for human beings because evolutionary theory is only concerned with biological processes, and the human soul is not biological, and therefore could not have evolved. Because it is transmaterial (transphysical), the soul also survives bodily death. Ample evidence for this may be found in the medical studies of near death experiences (see above Chapter Seven).

86. What about the existence of alien life elsewhere in the universe?

Given that there are 10^{22} stars in 10^{11} galaxies in our anthropic universe (designed for life), it is likely that there will be a large number of planets capable of sustaining a life form. This means that we cannot exclude the possibility of life forms on other planets. Though scientists are divided about this possibility, it seems possible that other highly complex life forms may exist in our universe.

If there were another life form on another planet which is capable of:
a. Self-consciousness,
b. Self-transcendence,
c. An awareness of: i. the infinite and eternal, and of
    ii. perfect truth, love, goodness, beauty, and being, and
d. If such a life form had a similar capacity to that of human beings to survive bodily death,

then we would have to suppose that they would also have a *soul* which did not evolve but came from God. If such beings existed, we would be expected, as Christians, to evangelize and baptize them if they were not aware of:
a. Love as the meaning of life,
b. God being unconditional love, and
c. Emmanuel—God with us—having come into our midst in a perfect act of unconditional love.

References

Clifford, Richard and Murphy, Roland 1990 "Genesis" in *The New Jerome Biblical Commentary* Ed. by Raymond Brown, et. al. (Englewood Cliffs, New Jersey: Prentice Hall).

Lepp, Ignace 1963. *Atheism in Our Time* (New York: Macmillan).

Lonergan, Bernard 1998. *Insight: A Study of Human Understanding* (Toronto: University of Toronto Press).

Maly, Eugene 1968. "Genesis" in *The Jerome Biblical Commentary* by Raymond Brown et. al. (Englewood Cliffs, New Jersey: Prentice Hall).

Markham, Ian 2010 *Against Atheism: Why Dawkins, Hitchens, and Harris are Fundamentally Wrong* (New Jersey: Wiley-Blackwell).

Pope Pius XII, 1943. *Divino Afflante Spiritu*.
http://www.vatican.va/holy_father/pius_xii/encyclicals/documents/hf_p-xii_enc_30091943_divino-afflante-spiritu_en.html

Pope Pius XII, 1950. *Humani Generis*.
http://www.vatican.va/holy_father/pius_xii/encyclicals/documents/hf_p-xii_enc_12081950_humani-generis_en.html

Appendix

Additional Questions and Answers about Jesus

Editor's Note: this material is not in the series from Nothing to Cosmos: God & Science. It was a response to a question asked in the Q&A session of Fr. Spitzer's live presentation Science, God, and Creation. It may be of interest to those studying both series, and so it is included.

Six Questions Leading Toward Jesus as Emmanuel

Many people ask, "If we can give evidence of an intelligent Creator, why is Jesus important?" In short, because Jesus reveals that this intelligent Creator is unconditionally loving. This reflection helps to pave the way from an intelligent Creator to Jesus' revelation of an unconditionally loving God.

1) **What is the most positive and creative power or capacity within us?**

   At first glance, one might want to respond that this power is intellect, or artistic creativity, but further reflection may show that the capacity to apprehend truth or knowledge, or to create beauty, *in and of itself*, is not necessarily positive. Knowledge and beauty can be misused, and therefore be negative, destructive, manipulative, inauthentic, and thus undermine both the individual and common good. There is but one human power that contains its own end of "positivity" within itself, one power that is directed toward the positive of itself, and therefore one power that directs intellect and artistic creativity to their proper, positive end. Love's capacity for empathy, its ability to enter into a unity with others leading to a natural "giving of self," forms the fabric of the common good and the human community, and so seeks as its end the good of both individuals and that community.

   Love by its very nature unifies, seeks the positive, orders things to their proper end, finds a harmony amidst diversity, and gives of itself in order to initiate and actualize this unifying purpose. This implies that love is naturally oriented toward perfect positivity and perfect fulfillment.

Furthermore, love would seem to be the one *virtue* that can be an end in itself. Other virtues do not *necessarily* culminate in a unity with others whereby doing the good for the other is just as easy if not easier than doing the good for oneself. Thus, courage, left to itself, might be mere bravado or might lead to the persecution of the weak. Self-discipline, left to itself, might lead to a disdain for the weak or a sense of self-sufficiency which is antithetical to empathy. Even humility can be overbearing and disdainful if it is not done out of love. Even though these virtues are necessary means for the actualization of love (i.e., authentic love cannot exist without courage, self-discipline, and humility), they cannot be ends in themselves, for they can be the instruments of unlove when they are not guided by the intrinsic goodness of love. Love seems to be the only virtue that can be an end in itself and therefore can stand by itself.

Now, if you, the reader, affirm the existence of this power within yourself and further affirm that it is the guiding light of both intellect and creativity, that its successful operation is the only way in which all your other powers can be guided to a positive end, that it is therefore the only way of guaranteeing positivity for both yourself and others, and that it therefore holds out the promise of authentic fulfillment, purpose in life, and happiness, then you will have acknowledged love to be the highest of all powers. You will then want to proceed to the next question.

2) **If love is the one power that seeks the positive in itself, and we are made to find our purpose in life through love, could God (perfect Being), who created us with this loving nature, be devoid of love?**

If the Creator were devoid of love, why would that Creator create human beings not only with the capacity for love, but to be fulfilled only when they are loving? If the Creator is devoid of love, why make love the actualization of all human powers and desires, and therefore of human nature? If the Creator is not loving, then the creation of "beings meant for love" seems absurd. However, if the Creator is loving, then creating a loving creature (i.e., sharing His loving nature) would seem to be both intrinsically and extrinsically consistent with what (or perhaps better, "who") He is. Could the Creator be any less loving than the "loving nature" He has created? Furthermore, if a Creator were perfect Being, wouldn't that perfect Being also be capable of the one power and virtue which can be an end in itself, that is, Love?

If you, the reader, can reasonably affirm the love of the Creator from the above, then you may want to proceed to the third question.

3) Is my desire to love and to be loved conditional or unconditional?

It may do well to pause for a moment here and give some background about our desire for love which has occupied the writings of many philosophers since the time of Plato.

We appear to have a desire for *perfect and unconditional Love*. Not only do we have the power to love (i.e., the power to be naturally connected to another human being in profound empathy, care, self-gift, concern, and acceptance), we have a "sense" of what this profound interpersonal connection would be like if it were perfect. This sense of perfect love has the positive effect of inciting us to pursue ever more perfect forms of love. However, it has the drawback of inciting us to *expect* ever more perfect love from other human beings. This generally leads to frustrated expectations of others and consequently to a decline of relationships that can never grow fast enough to match this expectation of perfect and unconditional Love.

The evidence of this desire for *perfect and unconditional Love* manifests itself in our frustrated expectations within relationships. Have you ever had this experience – where you thought a relationship (or friendship) with another was going quite well until little imperfections began to manifest themselves? In situations like these, there might be slight irritation, but one has hopes that the ideal will soon be recaptured. But as the fallibility of the beloved begins to be more acutely manifest (the other is not perfectly humble, gentle, kind, forgiving, self-giving, and concerned with me) the irritation becomes frustration, which, in turn, becomes dashed expectation: "I can't believe I thought she was really the One." Of course, she wasn't the One, because she is not perfect and unconditioned.

This gives rise to the question, "Why do we all too frequently expect our beloveds to be perfect and expect ourselves to be perfect to our beloveds if we did not have a desire for perfect and unconditional Love in the first place?" The reader must now apply this question to him or herself. If you did not have a desire for perfect and unconditional Love, why would you be so dissatisfied with imperfect and conditioned manifestations of love in others (even from the time of childhood)? If you sense within yourself an incapacity to be ultimately satisfied by any form of conditioned or finite love, then you will have also affirmed within yourself the intrinsic desire for unconditional Love, which leads to the next question.

4) If my desire for love can only be ultimately satisfied by unconditional Love, then could the Creator of this desire be anything less than Unconditional Love?

A simple response to this question might run as follows: if we assume that the Creator does not intend to frustrate this desire for unconditional Love within all of us, it would seem that His creation of the desire would imply an intention to fulfill it, which would, in turn, imply the very presence of this quality within Him. This would mean that the Creator of the desire for unconditional Love is (as the only possible fulfillment of that desire) Himself Unconditional Love. The reader here is only affirming the inconsistency of a "Creator incapable of unconditional Love" creating a being with the desire for perfect and unconditional Love. This is sufficient for affirming the presence of unconditional Love in the Creator.

A more complete explanation might begin with the *origin* of the desire for perfect and unconditional Love. The awareness of unconditional Love (which arouses the desire for unconditional Love) seems to be beyond any specifically known or concretely experienced love, for it seems to cause dissatisfaction with *every* conditioned love we have known or experienced. How can we have an awareness of love that we have neither known nor experienced? How can we even extrapolate to it if we do not know where we are going? The inability of philosophers to give a purely naturalistic answer to these questions has led them to associate the "tacit awareness of unconditional Love" with the "felt presence of Unconditional Love Itself." Unconditional Love Itself would therefore seem to be the cause of our awareness of It and also our desire for It. Inasmuch as Unconditional Love Itself transcends all conditioned (and human) manifestations of love, it might fairly be associated with the Creator. The Creator would then be associated with our human awareness of and desire for unconditional Love. Therefore, it seems that the Creator would have to be at least capable of unconditional Love.[55]

5) If the Creator is Unconditional Love, would He want to enter into a relationship with us of intense empathy, that is, would He want to be Emmanuel ("God with us")?

If one did not attribute unconditional Love to God, then the idea of God wanting to be with us, or God being with us, would be preposterous. A God of stoic indifference would not want to bother with creatures, let alone actually be among them and enter into empathetic relationship with them. However, in the logic of love, or rather, in the logic of unconditional Love, this changes.

If we attribute the various parts of the definition of *agapē* to an unconditionally loving Creator, we might obtain the following result: God (as Unconditional *Agapē*) would be unconditional empathy and care for others (even to the point of self-sacrificial care). God would seek unconditionally to protect, defend, maintain, and enhance the *intrinsic* dignity, worth, lovability, unique goodness, transcendental mystery, and intrinsic eternity of every one of us.

Love is empathizing with the other and entering into a unity with that other whereby doing the good for the other is just as easy, if not easier, than doing the good for oneself. This kind of love has the non-egocentricity, humility, self-gift, deep

---

[55] The simple and complete explanations of "unconditional Love in the Creator" may be combined to reveal God's intention to fulfill our desire for unconditional Love:

A) The Cause of the awareness of and desire for unconditional Love cannot be capable of only conditioned love. Therefore, the Cause would have to be at least capable of unconditional Love.

B) If the Cause of our awareness of and desire for unconditional love is truly capable of unconditional Love, then He would not have created us with this awareness and desire only to frustrate it (for this would contradict the nature of Unconditional Love).

C) Therefore, the unconditionally loving Creator of our awareness of and desire for unconditional Love intends to fulfill that desire unconditionally.

affection, and care which would make infinite power into infinite gentleness, and would incite an infinitely powerful Being to enter into a restrictive condition to empathize more fully with His beloveds. In this logic, "Emmanuel" ("God with us") would be typical of an unconditionally loving God. This would characterize the way that Unconditional Love would act – not being egocentrically conscious of the infinite distance between Creator and creature, but rather being infinitely desirous of bridging this gap in a perfect unity of perfect empathy and perfect care. It would be just like the unconditionally loving God to be "God with us."

The following consideration might help to clarify this. If God is truly Unconditional Love, then it would not be unreasonable to suspect that He would be unconditional empathy; and if He were unconditional empathy, it would not be unreasonable to suspect that He would want to enter into an empathetic relationship with us "face-to-face" ("peer-to-peer") where the Lover and beloved would have a parallel access to the uniquely good and lovable personhood and mystery of the other (through empathy). A truly unconditionally loving Being would want to give *complete* empathetic access to His heart and interior life in a way which was proportionate to the receiving apparatus of the weaker (creaturely) being. It would seem reasonable (according to the reasonings of the heart), then, that an unconditionally loving Creator would want to be Emmanuel in order to give us complete empathetic access to that unconditional Love through voice, face, touch, action, concrete relationship, and in every other way that love, care, affection, home, and felt response can be concretely manifest and appropriated by us. If God really is Unconditional Love, then we might be presumptuous enough to expect that He might be Emmanuel; and if Emmanuel, then concretely manifest in history. If this resonates with the reader's thoughts and feelings, you will want to proceed to the next question.

6) If it would be typical of the unconditionally loving God to want to be fully with us, then is Jesus the One?

As reasonable and responsible as the answers to the above questions might be, they can be considerably strengthened through historical corroboration, that is, through experienceable data which concretizes the reasoning given immediately above. What kind of experienceable data could accomplish this corroboration? Data which at once manifests (1) God in our midst (Emmanuel) and (2) God as Unconditional Love. It so happens that a remarkably powerful experienceable event did at once manifest and synthesize these two corroborating data, and showed the above reasoning about the unconditional Love of God to be both reasonable and experienceable, and to be mutually corroboratable through concrete experience and the logic of love. This remarkable experienceable event is *Jesus Christ.*

What is the evidence that Jesus is Emmanuel ("God with us")?

In brief, the answer is

(a) Jesus' resurrection in glory and spirit,
(b) Jesus' gift of the Holy Spirit,
(c) Jesus' miracles – particularly the raisings from the dead,
(d) Jesus' self-proclamation of being the exclusive son of the Father, the definitive bringer of the Kingdom of God, and His claim to complete the mission reserved for Yahweh alone.

The historicity of these four signs and the rationale for believing that these four signs indicate his divinity can be found on the Magis Center of Reason and Faith website – **www.magisreasonfaith.org**. Simply click on the tab "encyclopedias" and then select the second option about evidence for Jesus' divinity and love, then refer to the articles in **2.2 through 2.7**.

What is the evidence that Jesus is unconditional love and that He revealed the Father to be unconditional love?

In brief, the answer is connected to:

(a) His revelation of love as the highest commandment (and His link of the love of God to love of neighbor and self),
(b) His definition of love in the Beatitudes and the parables about love (such as the Good Samaritan),
(c) His miracles (acts of healing compassion),
(d) His passion and death (an act of complete self-sacrifice

which He interpreted to be an act of unconditional love),

(e) His gift of the Holy Eucharist (which he interpreted to be the vehicle through which his transforming personhood and unconditional love would be given to all subsequent generations), and

(f) His revelation of the Father's unconditional love by naming him "Abba" (Daddy), the parable of the Prodigal's Son (in which the father of the son is His revelation of who God the Father is) and his name for himself ("the beloved one" implying that the Father is the one who loves the beloved").

The historicity of these signs and the rationale for why they point to the unconditional love of Jesus and the Father can be found on the Magis Center of Reason and Faith website – **www.magisreasonfaith.org**. Simply click on the tab "encyclopedias," then select the second option about evidence for Jesus' divinity and love, and then refer to the articles in **2.9 through 2.12**.